TEACHER EDITION

W9-CPE-477

Printed in U.S.A.

ISBN 978-0-547-59223-7

7 8 9 10 1420 20 19 18 17 16 15 14 13 12

4500352307   C D E F G

HOUGHTON MIFFLIN HARCOURT

Number and Operations

COMMON CORE · **CRITICAL AREA** Representing, relating, and operating on whole numbers, initially with sets of objects

Domain: Operations and Algebraic Thinking   CC.K.OA

Lessons   **Grade K Common Core State Standards**

5.1–5.3   **Understand addition as putting together and adding to, and understand subtraction as taking apart and taking from.**
CC.K.OA.1   Represent addition and subtraction with objects, fingers, mental images, drawings, sounds (e.g., claps), acting out situations, verbal explanations, expressions, or equations.

5.4, 5.6   **Understand addition as putting together and adding to, and understand subtraction as taking apart and taking from.**
CC.K.OA.5   Fluently add and subtract within 5.

5.5   **Understand addition as putting together and adding to, and understand subtraction as taking apart and taking from.**
CC.K.OA.4   For any number from 1 to 9, find the number that makes 10 when added to the given number, e.g., by using objects or drawings, and record the answer with a drawing or equation.

5.7   **Understand addition as putting together and adding to, and understand subtraction as taking apart and taking from.**
CC.K.OA.2   Solve addition and subtraction word problems, and add and subtract within 10, e.g., by using objects or drawings to represent the problem.

5.8–5.12   **Understand addition as putting together and adding to, and understand subtraction as taking apart and taking from.**
CC.K.OA.3   Decompose numbers less than or equal to 10 into pairs in more than one way, e.g., by using objects or drawings, and record each decomposition by a drawing or equation (e.g., $5 = 2 + 3$ and $5 = 4 + 1$).

Table of Contents

Chapter 5 Addition

 Domain:
Operations and Algebraic Thinking   CC.K.OA

Mathematical Practices:
CC.K–12.MP.2   Reason abstractly and quantitatively.
CC.K–12.MP.4   Model with mathematics.

Chapter At A Glance

Domain: Operations and Algebraic Thinking

Chapter Essential Question How can you show addition?

Use the Chapter Planner in the *Go Math! Planning Guide* for pacing.

Lesson At A Glance

	LESSON 5.1 CC.K.OA.1	**LESSON 5.2** CC.K.OA.1	**LESSON 5.3** CC.K.OA.1
	Addition: Add to 169A	**Hands on • Addition: Put Together 173A**	**Problem Solving • Act Out Addition Problems 177A**
Essential Question	How can you show addition as adding to?	How can you show addition as putting together?	How can you solve problems using the strategy *act it out?*
Objective	Use expressions to represent addition within 5.	Use expressions to represent addition.	Solve problems by using the strategy *act it out.*
Vocabulary	**add**	**plus**	**is equal to,** plus
Materials	MathBoard, two-color counters, Counting Tape	MathBoard, two-color counters, Counting Tape	MathBoard, Counting Tape

Print Resources

5.1 Student Edition	5.2 Student Edition	5.3 Student Edition
5.1 Standards Practice Book	5.2 Standards Practice Book	5.3 Standards Practice Book
5.1 Reteach	5.2 Reteach	5.3 Reteach
5.1 Enrich	5.2 Enrich	5.3 Enrich
Grab-and-Go™ Centers Kit	Grab-and-Go™ Centers Kit	Grab-and-Go™ Centers Kit
ELL Strategy • Describe	**ELL** Strategy • Rephrase	**ELL** Strategy • Describe

Digital Path

5.1 *e*Student Edition	5.2 *e*Student Edition	5.3 *e*Student Edition
5.1 *e*Teacher Edition	5.2 *e*Teacher Edition	5.3 *e*Teacher Edition
		i**T**iTools

Response to Intervention

Before the Chapter	During the Lesson	After the Chapter
✓ **Show What You Know**	✓ **Share and Show**	✓ **Chapter Review/Test**
• **Prerequisite Skills Activities**	• **RtI Activities**	• **RtI Activities**
• **Soar to Success Math**	• **Mid-Chapter Checkpoint**	• **Soar to Success Math**
	• **Soar to Success Math**	

EVERY DAY COUNTS®

Use every day to develop computational fluency.
Visit www.greatsource.com/everydaycounts

Assess Depth of Knowledge

See Chapter 5 Performance Task and *Assessment Guide*.

LESSON 5.4 CC.K.OA.5	**LESSON 5.5** CC.K.OA.4	**LESSON 5.6** CC.K.OA.5
Hands on: Algebra • Model and Draw Addition Problems 181A	**Algebra • Write Addition Sentences for 10** 185A	**Algebra • Write Addition Sentences** 189A
How can you use objects and drawings to solve addition word problems?	How can you use a drawing to find the number that makes a 10 from a given number?	How can you solve addition word problems and complete the addition sentence?
Use objects and drawings to solve addition word problems within 5.	Use a drawing to find 10 from a given number and record the equation.	Solve addition word problems within 5 and record the equation.
plus, is equal to	plus, is equal to	plus, is equal to
MathBoard, connecting cubes, Counting Tape	MathBoard, Counting Tape	MathBoard, Counting Tape

5.4 Student Edition	**5.5 Student Edition**	**5.6 Student Edition**
5.4 Standards Practice Book	**5.5 Standards Practice Book**	**5.6 Standards Practice Book**
5.4 Reteach	5.5 Reteach	5.6 Reteach
5.4 Enrich	5.5 Enrich	5.6 Enrich
Grab-and-Go™ Centers Kit	**Grab-and-Go™ Centers Kit**	**Grab-and-Go™ Centers Kit**
ELL Strategy • Model Language	**ELL Strategy •** Draw	**ELL Strategy •** Model Concepts

5.4 eStudent Edition	**5.5 eStudent Edition**	**5.6 eStudent Edition**
5.4 eTeacher Edition	**5.5 eTeacher Edition**	**5.6 eTeacher Edition**
Animated Math Models	Animated Math Models	Animated Math Models
iTools	iTools	iTools
HMH Mega Math	HMH Mega Math	

GREAT ON INTERACTIVE WHITEBOARD!

Digital Path

- Animated Math Models
- Assessment
- HMH Mega Math
- iTools
- Multimedia *eGlossary*
- Professional Development Video Podcasts
- Soar to Success Math

Chapter At A Glance

Domain: Operations and Algebraic Thinking

Lesson At A Glance

	LESSON 5.7 CC.K.OA.2	**LESSON 5.8** CC.K.OA.3	**LESSON 5.9** CC.K.OA.3
	Algebra • Write More Addition Sentences 193A	**Hands On: Algebra • Number Pairs to 5** 197A	**Hands On: Algebra • Number Pairs for 6 and 7** 201A
Essential Question	How can you solve addition word problems and complete the addition sentence?	How can you model and write addition sentences for number pairs for sums to 5?	How can you model and write addition sentences for number pairs for each sum of 6 and 7?
Objective	Solve addition word problems within 10 and record the equation.	Decompose numbers within 5 into pairs in more than one way and record each decomposition with an equation.	Decompose 6 and 7 into pairs in more than one way and record each decomposition with an equation.
Vocabulary	plus, is equal to	plus, is equal to, one, two, three, four, five, pair	plus, is equal to, one, two, three, four, five, pair, six, seven
Materials	MathBoard, Counting Tape	MathBoard, connecting cubes, Counting Tape	MathBoard, connecting cubes, Counting Tape

Print Resources

5.7 Student Edition	5.8 Student Edition	5.9 Student Edition
5.7 Standards Practice Book	5.8 Standards Practice Book	5.9 Standards Practice Book
5.7 Reteach	5.8 Reteach	5.9 Reteach
5.7 Enrich	5.8 Enrich	5.9 Enrich
Grab-and-Go™ Centers Kit	Grab-and-Go™ Centers Kit	Grab-and-Go™ Centers Kit
ELL Strategy • Identify Relationships	**ELL** Strategy • Describe	**ELL** Strategy • Model Concepts

Digital Path

5.7 *e*Student Edition	5.8 *e*Student Edition	5.9 *e*Student Edition
5.7 *e*Teacher Edition	5.8 *e*Teacher Edition	5.9 *e*Teacher Edition
Animated Math Models	Animated Math Models	Animated Math Models
*i*Tools	*i*Tools	*i*Tools
HMH Mega Math		

Assessment

Diagnostic	**Formative**	**Summative**
• Show What You Know	• Lesson Quick Check	• Chapter Review/Test
• Diagnostic Interview Task	• Mid-Chapter Checkpoint	• Performance Assessment
• Soar to Success Math		• Chapter Test
		• Online Assessment

How can you model and write addition sentences for number pairs for sums of 8?

Decompose 8 into pairs in more than one way and record each decomposition with an equation.

plus, is equal to, one, two, three, four, five, pair, six, seven, eight

MathBoard, connecting cubes, Counting Tape

5.10 Student Edition
5.10 Standards Practice Book
5.10 Reteach
5.10 Enrich
Grab-and-Go™ Centers Kit
ELL Strategy • Restate

5.10 eStudent Edition
5.10 eTeacher Edition
▣ **Animated Math Models**
iT iTools

How can you model and write addition sentences for number pairs for sums of 9?

Decompose 9 into pairs in more than one way and record each decomposition with an equation.

plus, is equal to, one, two, three, four, five, pair, six, seven, eight, nine

MathBoard, connecting cubes, Counting Tape

5.11 Student Edition
5.11 Standards Practice Book
5.11 Reteach
5.11 Enrich
Grab-and-Go™ Centers Kit
ELL Strategy • Model Concepts

5.11 eStudent Edition
5.11 eTeacher Edition
▣ **Animated Math Models**
iT iTools

How can you model and write addition sentences for number pairs for sums of 10?

Decompose 10 into pairs in more than one way and record each decomposition with an equation.

plus, is equal to, one, two, three, four, five, pair, six, seven, eight, nine, ten

MathBoard, connecting cubes, Counting Tape

5.12 Student Edition
5.12 Standards Practice Book
5.12 Reteach
5.12 Enrich
Grab-and-Go™ Centers Kit
ELL Strategy • Describe

5.12 eStudent Edition
5.12 eTeacher Edition
✓ **Chapter 5 Test**
▣ **Animated Math Models**
iT iTools
𝍌 **HMH Mega Math**

 **PROFESSIONAL DEVELOPMENT** COMMON CORE

Teaching for Depth

by Juli K. Dixon
Professor of Mathematics Education
University of Central Florida
Orlando, Florida

Joining Problems

Children explore addition through situations that require a joining action.

- Making cube trains of two colors to model addition is one way to show joining sets.

- Children use pictures of two sets to record the addition sentence using both symbols and words. They circle the two sets to reinforce the concept of addition as joining.

- Children also create their own problems and record the number sentences. This activity helps to evaluate their understanding of addition and their ability to correctly record a number sentence.

Number Pairs

Children make sense of decomposing numbers as they make number pairs.

- Given a number like 3, they find the number that makes 10 when added to 3. This experience will lead to addition strategies like "make a 10" in later grades.

- Children explore number pairs by representing a number such as 8 with two different colors of cubes. They might use three red cubes and five blue cubes or six red cubes and two blue cubes.

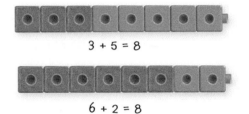

$$3 + 5 = 8$$

$$6 + 2 = 8$$

- Students record their thinking using number sentences.

Modeling Sums

Experience modeling sums with concrete objects is an important part of learning to add. Children will rely less on models as they build an understanding of addition.

From the Research

❝Students begin their study of number situations by modeling problems directly, using the context to shape their concrete and often cumbersome methods. They gradually move toward representing problems more abstractly.❞ (NRC, 2001, p. 217)

COMMON CORE

Mathematical Practices

Children solve problems with contexts that require them to add to a set as well as to put together sets. How they solve the problems depends on the context of the word problems themselves. When children model problems they learn how to **make sense of problems and persevere in solving them.**

 PODCASTING

 Professional Development Video Podcasts
The Meaning of Addition and Subtraction, Grades K–2, Segment 2

Cross-Curricular Center Activities

Cloud Addition

Objective Use clouds to understand addition.

Materials blue construction paper, cotton balls

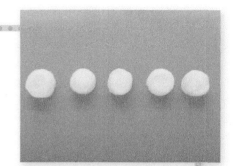

- Explain that clouds are made from water. This water can fall as rain or snow.
- Supply children with paper and cotton. Explain that they are going to place clouds in the sky.
- Have children place two clouds, then additional clouds, in the sky. Have them identify that they added.
- Have children repeat the activity with different numbers of clouds.

Technology Center

Addition

Objective Explore addition.

Materials *i*Tools: Counters

- Have children use the Add Activity in *i*Tools.
- On the left side of the screen, children have a wide variety of counters from which to choose. To begin addition within 10, children click on their choice and stamp a set of counters above the *plus* symbol. They can then click on the same counter or choose a different one to stamp a set below the *plus* symbol.
- Have children click the Add button to see a total number of counters. Have them enter their answer in the sum box. They can then check their answer by clicking on the Check button.

Art Center

Ten Birds on a Fence

Objective Create and model addition problems.

Materials masking tape, at least two colors of connecting cubes

- Place a strip of masking tape across a table or the rug. Tell children to pretend that the tape is a fence where birds like to sit, and that the connecting cubes are colorful birds.
- Have one child place from one to nine birds of the same color on the fence. The other child helps some birds of a different color fly to the fence to make ten birds. A third child completes an addition sentence on the board.
- Have children repeat the activity several times. Then ask them to draw a picture of ten birds on a fence. There should be two different colors of birds. Ask them to complete an addition sentence that the picture shows.

Review Prerequisite Skills

 **RtI**

Activities

Fingers, Cubes, and Symbols `TIER 2`

Objective Use Number and Symbol Tiles to show numbers through 10.
Materials connecting cubes, Number and Symbol Tiles (front) (see *eTeacher Resources*)

Have children show numbers 5 to 10 with their fingers. Show them how to show all five fingers on their left hands and say *five*. Then have them show 6 with five fingers on the left hand and one finger on the right hand; have them say *six*. Continue the process until children have shown ten fingers.

Have children use their cubes and number tiles. Have them make a five-cube train.

- **Now make 6. Use the five-cube train. How many more cubes do you need to make 6?** 5 and one more make 6.

Have children place the one extra cube below the five-cube train. Have them match the number tile 6 to their cubes that represent 6.

Continue having children show numbers 7 to 10 using their five-cube trains and more cubes to form each number and match it to its number tile.

- **Two five-cube trains make what number?** 10 **A five-cube train and three more cubes make what number?** 8

 Math Expressions
Model from *Math Expressions*. For more information visit **www.eduplace.com/ hmhschool/mathexpressions**

Many Ways to Make 7 `TIER 2`

Objective Use cubes to show different ways to make 7.
Materials two colors of connecting cubes

Have children work in groups of 3 or 4. Ask them to make seven-cube trains using two colors of cubes. When they have made a cube train, they should check it with others in the group.

- **Did you make a cube train with seven cubes? Is it like the other seven-cube trains, or different from the other seven-cube trains? How many of each color did you use?**

Challenge children to make 7 many different ways.

 **COMMON CORE** **Common Core State Standards Across the Grades**

Before	Grade K	After
• Explore putting together sets.	**Domain: Operations and Algebraic Thinking** Understand addition as putting together and adding to, and understand subtraction as taking apart and taking from. **CC.K.OA.1, CC.K.OA.2, CC.K.OA.3, CC.K.OA.4, CC.K.OA.5**	**Domain: Operations and Algebraic Thinking** Understand and apply properties of operations and the relationship between addition and subtraction. **CC.1.OA.3** Add and subtract within 20. **CC.1.OA.5, CC.1.OA.6** Work with addition and subtraction equations. **CC.1.OA.7, CC.1.OA.8**

See A page of each lesson for Common Core Standard text.

Developing Math Language

Chapter Vocabulary

add to join two sets

is equal to a number or amount that is the same as

plus add to; a symbol that shows addition

pair set of two

six one greater than five; one less than seven

seven one greater than six; one less than eight

eight one greater than seven; one less than nine

nine one greater than eight; one less than ten

ten one greater than nine; one less than eleven

 Multimedia eGlossary

ELL Vocabulary Activity

Materials Vocabulary Card for *add* (see *eTeacher Resources*), pattern blocks

Objective Understand the math term *add*.

Place a set of three blocks on the table. Place another set of five blocks. Explain that you add when you put two sets together. Push the two sets together. **3 and 5 is 8.** Have children put together two sets of blocks. Ask how many blocks they have now.

Practice vocabulary by using questioning strategies such as:

Beginning
- Push together a set of two blocks and a set of three blocks. **If I add 2 + 3, how many blocks do I have in all? Count with me to find out.** 5

Intermediate
- **Add 4 + 1.** 5

Advanced
- **When you add 2 + 4, what are the two sets that you are putting together?** 2, 4 **How many do you have in all?** 6

See **ELL** Activity Guide for leveled activities.

Vocabulary Strategy • Graphic Organizer

Materials Word Analysis Graphic Organizer (see *eTeacher Resources*)

Have children complete the Word Analysis graphic organizer using the vocabulary word *plus*. In the first column, they should define the word. In the second column, they should draw a picture.

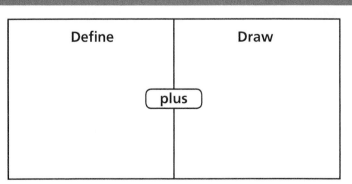

Define	Draw
plus	

Chapter 5

Introduce the Chapter

Curious About Math with Curious George

Most ladybugs have red, orange, or yellow wing covers and black spots.

• **How many ladybugs do you see?** 2

Additional facts about ladybugs:

• Ladybugs are beetles, which are insects.
• The ladybug uses its antennae to touch, smell, and taste.

Ask the following question to guide children to an answer.

• **If each ladybug has two antennae, how can you use cubes to show the number of antennae two ladybugs have?** two sets of two cubes

• **How many cubes will you have if you put together two sets?** 4

Chapter 5 — Addition

Curious About Math with Curious George

Most ladybugs have red, orange, or yellow wing covers and black spots.

• How many ladybugs do you see? 2

Intervention Options  **RtI** Response to Intervention

Use **Show What You Know**, **Lesson Quick Check**, and **Assessments** to diagnose children's intervention levels.

TIER 1	TIER 2	TIER 3	ENRICHMENT
On-Level Intervention	**Strategic Intervention**	**Intensive Intervention**	**Independent Activities**
For children who are generally at grade level but need early intervention with the lesson concepts, use:	For children who need small group instruction to review concepts and skills needed for the chapter, use:	For children who need one-on-one instruction to build foundational skills for the chapter, use:	For children who successfully complete lessons, use:

 Tier 1 Activity for every lesson

 Soar to Success Math

 Tier 2 Activity for every lesson

 Strategic Intervention Guide

 Prerequisite Skills Activities

Soar to Success Math

 Intensive Intervention Guide

 Soar to Success Math

Differentiated Centers Kit

• Enrich Activity for every lesson
• Enrich Book
 HMH Mega Math

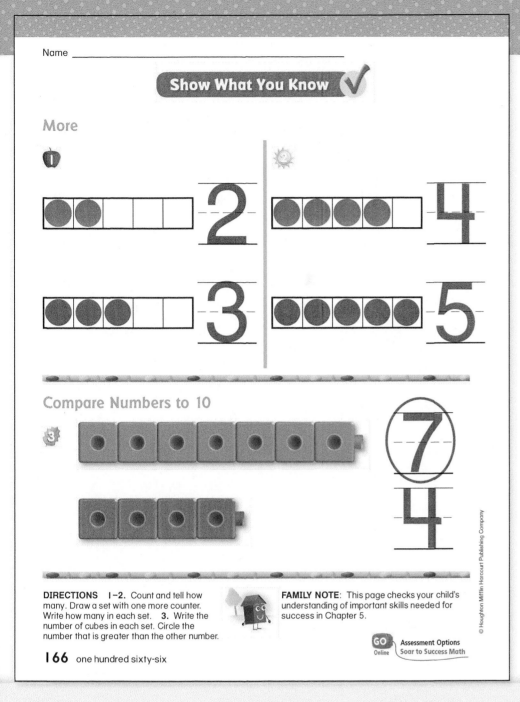

Name _____

Show What You Know ✔

More

① 2

3

☀ 4

5

Compare Numbers to 10

7

4

DIRECTIONS 1–2. Count and tell how many. Draw a set with one more counter. Write how many in each set. **3.** Write the number of cubes in each set. Circle the number that is greater than the other number.

GO Online — Assessment Options — Soar to Success Math

166 one hundred sixty-six

Assessing Prior Knowledge

Have children complete on their own **Show What You Know.** Tested items are the prerequisite skills of this chapter.

Diagnostic Interview Task

The alternative interview tasks below evaluate children's understanding of each **Show What You Know** skill. The diagnostic chart may be used for intervention or prerequisite skills.

Materials two-color counters, Workmat 2 (five frames), Numeral Cards (0–7) (see *eTeacher Resources*), connecting cubes

For evaluation checklist see *Assessment Guide.*

Place two counters in a five frame. Ask the child how many counters there are. Then ask the child to add one more.

- **Now how many counters are there?** 3

Show the child a green cube train with four cubes. Have the child tell you how many cubes are in the cube train. Place the numeral card for 4 next to the cube train. Show the child a yellow cube train with two cubes. Have the child tell you how many cubes are in the cube train. Place the numeral card for 2 next to the cube train.

- **Which number is greater?** 4

✔ Show What You Know • Diagnostic Assessment

Use to determine if children need intervention for the chapter's prerequisite skills.

Were children successful with Show What You Know?

If NO...then INTERVENE

If YES...then use INDEPENDENT ACTIVITIES

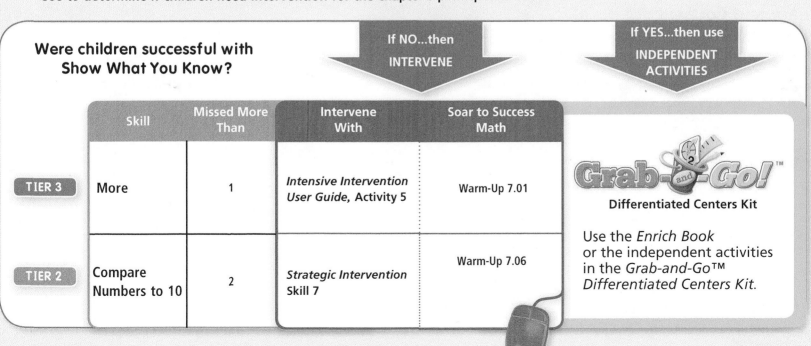

	Skill	Missed More Than	Intervene With	Soar to Success Math
TIER 3	More	1	*Intensive Intervention User Guide,* Activity 5	Warm-Up 7.01
TIER 2	Compare Numbers to 10	2	*Strategic Intervention* Skill 7	Warm-Up 7.06

Grab-and-Go!™

Differentiated Centers Kit

Use the *Enrich Book* or the independent activities in the *Grab-and-Go™ Differentiated Centers Kit.*

Vocabulary Builder

Children use multiple strategies to develop grade-appropriate vocabulary.

Have children complete the activities on this page by working alone or with partners.

Look at the page with children.

- **How many birds are on the ground?** 7

Have children show the number with a blue cube train and then write the number.

- **How many birds are flying?** 3

Have children show the number with a red cube train and then write the number.

Have children put together the cube trains and count the cubes. Explain that 7 and 3 are a pair of numbers that make 10.

Name _____

Vocabulary Builder

7 3   **ten**

© Houghton Mifflin Harcourt Publishing Company

DIRECTIONS Count and tell how many birds are on the ground. Count and tell how many birds are flying. Write these numbers to show a pair of numbers that make ten.

GO Online • eStudent Edition • Multimedia eGlossary

Chapter 5   one hundred sixty-seven **167**

Literature Big Book

Quack and Count
by Keith Baker
reinforces addition
for Chapter 5.

Game Pairs That Make 7

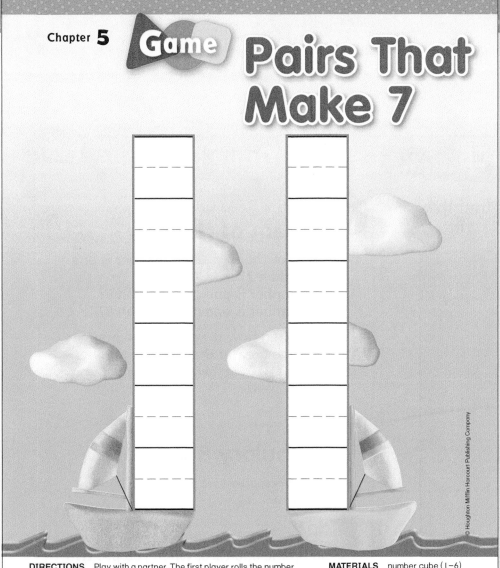

DIRECTIONS Play with a partner. The first player rolls the number cube and writes the number on the yellow boat. Partners determine what number makes 7 when paired with the number on the yellow boat. Players take turns rolling the number cube until that number is rolled. Write the number beside it on the green boat. Partners continue to roll the number cube finding pairs of numbers that make 7.

MATERIALS number cube (1–6)

168 one hundred sixty-eight

Game Pairs That Make 7

▶ Using the Game

Set up a game center in the classroom. Include *Pairs That Make 7*, along with the materials needed to play.

Materials Number Cube (1–6)

The first player rolls the number cube and writes the number on the yellow boat. Partners determine what number makes 7 when paired with the number on the yellow boat.

Players take turns rolling the number cube until that number is rolled. Write the number beside it on the green boat.

Partners continue to roll the number cube finding pairs of numbers that make 7.

Standards Practice

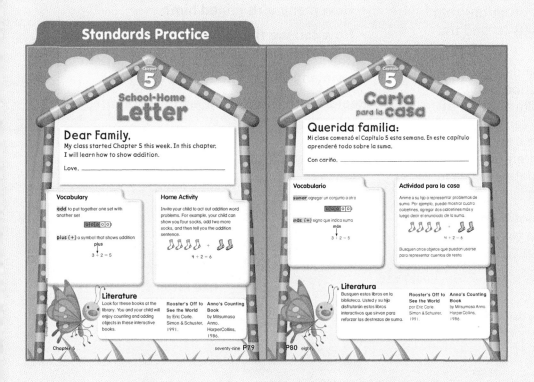

School-Home Letter available in English and Spanish in the *Standards Practice Book*, pp. P79–P80

The letter provides families with an overview of the math in the chapter, math vocabulary, an activity, and literature to read together.

Addition: Add to

LESSON AT A GLANCE

Common Core Standard
Understand addition as putting together and adding to, and understand subtraction as taking apart and taking from.
CC.K.OA.1 Represent addition and subtraction with objects, fingers, mental images, drawings, sounds (e.g., claps), acting out situations, verbal explanations, expressions, or equations.

Materials
MathBoard

Lesson Objective
Use expressions to represent addition within 5.

Essential Question
How can you show addition as adding to?

Vocabulary
add

Digital Path

 *eStudent Edition*

PROFESSIONAL DEVELOPMENT
COMMON CORE

About the Math

Why Teach This

Addition is the first operation that children encounter in school. In this chapter, we present addition situations that represent adding to and putting together sets to find the sum—the total, or how many in all.

Addition is easy for children to model and understand because it can be represented by physical actions: Two children can join three other children to make a group of five children (an adding situation). Children can put together two red cubes and three blue cubes to make a cube train of five cubes. In the dramatic play center, children can place two plates on a table, and then add three plates—to have five plates altogether—when "company" comes.

Children should also be given sets that cannot be physically joined. We are not likely to be able to move two trees in a front yard and three trees in a back yard, yet we can add to find how many there are in all.

 Professional Development Video Podcasts

Daily Routines
Math Board

Common Core
SPIRAL REVIEW

Problem of the Day
eTransparency 5.1

Number of the Day What number is one greater than 2?
What number is one greater than 6?
What number is one greater than 8? 3, 7, 9

Ask children how they can find a number that is one greater than a given number. Count forward by one. Think of the number that comes next when counting.

Vocabulary Builder

Materials Vocabulary Card for *add* (see *eTeacher Resources*)

Add

Hold up the *add* card. **When you put two sets or two numbers together, you add them.**

Have one boy come to the front of the class.

- **How many boys are there?** 1

Now ask one girl to join him.

- **How many girls joined him?** 1
- **How can we find how many children there are now?** add

How many children are there now? 2

Repeat with other numbers of children.

Literature

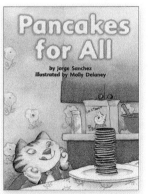
Pancakes for All

From the Grab-and-Go™ Differentiated Centers Kit

Children will read the book and count the five kittens.

Differentiated Instruction Activities

ⒺⓁⓁ Language Support
🕐 Visual / Linguistic
Small Group

Strategy: Describe

Materials connecting cubes

Children can practice their comprehension by describing in words what they have seen.

- Have children make a green two-cube train.

- Have children add one orange cube to the train and describe the train. The cube train has two green cubes and one orange cube.

- You can also say that the cube train has three cubes. Have children repeat this phrase.

Repeat with other examples.

See ⒺⓁⓁ Activity Guide for leveled activities.

Enrich
🕐 Kinesthetic
Partners

Materials connecting cubes, paper bag

Give partners a paper bag and five cubes.

- Ask one partner to take out no more than four cubes.

- Have the other partner take out the remaining cubes.

- Ask partners to make two sets of cubes and to write the numbers that represent their sets of cubes. Have them write how many cubes there are now.

Have partners take turns being first to take out some cubes.

3 and 2
5

▲RtI Response to Intervention

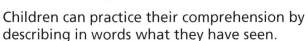

Reteach Tier 1
🕐 Kinesthetic / Visual
Whole Class / Small Group

Materials self-stick notes

Have children use numbers to represent addition word problems.

- On the board write: ____ and ____ and below that write: ____.

- Tell the following word problem as you act it out.

- **There is one book on the desk. Then I place four more books on the desk. How many books are on the desk now?**

- Call on volunteers one at a time to write a number on a self-stick note and place it on the board in the correct place.

Repeat with other addition word problems with sums to 5 or less.

Tier 2
🕐 Kinesthetic / Visual
Small Group

Materials Numeral Cards (0-7) (see *eTeacher Resources*), pictures with sets of five or fewer objects or people

Children will represent addition word problems with numbers.

- Show a picture that shows a simple addition word problem. For example, three sheep in a field and one horse in a barn.

- Ask a simple word problem to match the picture. **Three animals were in the field and one more came. How many animals are there now?**

- Have children select a numeral card that matches each of the sets in the word problem. Then have them choose the numeral card that shows how many there are now.

1 ENGAGE

Access Prior Knowledge Have a group of two boys come to the front of the classroom. Then have a group of three girls come to the front of the classroom. As you point to the groups, ask:

- **How many boys are in this group?** 2
- **How many girls are in this group?** 3

Continue with other groups of boys and girls using numbers 10 or less.

2 TEACH and TALK

▶ Listen and Draw (MATHEMATICAL PRACTICES)

Read this problem aloud as children listen.

There are two children on the swings. One more child comes. How many children are there now?

- **How many children are on the swings?** 2
- **Trace the number.**
- **How many children are being added to the group?** 1
- **Trace the number.**

Explain that when you put two groups together, such as 2 and 1, you add to find how many there are now.

- **What word can you use when you put together two groups?** add
- **What word tells you to add?** and
- **What is 2 and 1?** 3 **Trace the number.**

Model how to point to each child on the page as you count aloud with the children to find how many children there are now; **1, 2, 3.**

 COMMON CORE

CC.K.OA.1 Represent addition and subtraction with objects, fingers, mental images, drawings, sounds (e.g., claps), acting out situations, verbal explanations, expressions, or equations.

Name _____

Lesson 5.1

Addition: Add To

Essential Question How can you show addition as adding to?

COMMON CORE STANDARD CC.K.OA.1
Understand addition as putting together and adding to, and understand subtraction as taking apart and taking from.

Listen and Draw REAL WORLD

2 and 1
3

DIRECTIONS Listen to the addition word problem. Trace the number that shows how many children are on the swings. Trace the number that shows how many children are being added to the group. Trace the number that shows how many children there are now.

Check children's work.

Chapter 5 · Lesson 1

one hundred sixty-nine **169**

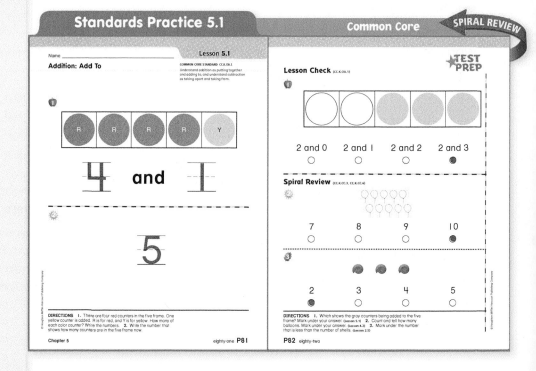

Standards Practice 5.1

Common Core SPIRAL REVIEW

Name _____

Addition: Add To

COMMON CORE STANDARD CC.K.OA.1
Understand addition as putting together and adding to, and understand subtraction as taking apart and taking from.

4 and 1

5

DIRECTIONS 1. There are four red counters in the five frame. One yellow counter is added. R is for red, and Y is for yellow. How many of each color counter? Write the numbers. 2. Write the number that shows how many counters are in the five frame now.

Chapter 5

eighty-one **P81**

Lesson Check (CC.K.OA.1)

★TEST PREP

2 and 0	2 and 1	2 and 2	2 and 3
○	○	○	●

Spiral Review (CC.K.CC.3, CC.K.CC.6)

7	8	9	10
○	○	○	●

2	3	4	5
●	○	○	○

DIRECTIONS 1. Which shows the gray counters being added to the five frame? Mark under your answer. (Lesson 5.1) 2. Count and tell how many balloons. Mark under your answer. (Lesson 4.2) 3. Mark under the number that is less than the number of shells. (Lesson 2.5)

P82 eighty-two

Share and Show

1

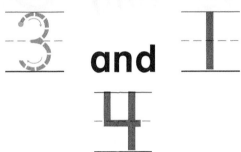

3 **and** 1

4

· ·

DIRECTIONS 1. Listen to the addition word problem. Trace the number that shows how many children are sitting eating lunch. Write the number that shows how many children are being added to the group. Write the number that shows how many children are having lunch now.

170 one hundred seventy

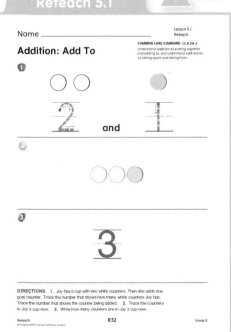

Reteach 5.1

Name _____
Lesson 5.1
Reteach

Addition: Add To
COMMON CORE STANDARD CC.K.OA.1
Understand addition as putting together and adding to, and understand subtraction as taking apart and taking from.

1 ◯◯ ⬤

2 **and** 1

2 ◯◯⬤

3 3

DIRECTIONS 1. Joy has a cup with two white counters. Then she adds one gray counter. Trace the number that shows how many white counters Joy has. 2. Trace the counters in Joy's cup now. 3. Write how many counters are in Joy's cup now.

Reteach   R32   Grade K
© Houghton Mifflin Harcourt Publishing Company

Enrich 5.1

Name _____
Lesson 5.1
Enrich

Caterpillar Counters
COMMON CORE STANDARD CC.K.OA.1
Understand addition as putting together and adding to, and understand subtraction as taking apart and taking from.

1 R Y Y Y

1 **and** 3   Check children's work.

2 Y Y R R R

2 **and** 3   Check children's work.

3 R R Y

2 **and** 1   Check children's work.

DIRECTIONS 1-3. Place two-color counters as shown. R is for red, and Y is for yellow. How many of each color did you use? Write the numbers. Tell a friend how many counters are on the caterpillar now. Color the caterpillar to show the counters.

Enrich   E32   Grade K
© Houghton Mifflin Harcourt Publishing Company

---

3 **PRACTICE**

▶ **Share and Show • Guided Practice**

Read this addition word problem aloud to children.

There are three children eating lunch. One more child comes. How many children are having lunch now?

- **How many children are eating lunch?** 3 **Trace the number.**
- **How many children are being added to the group?** 1
- **Write the number.**
- **What will you have to do to find how many children there are now?** add

Have children count all of the children.

- **What is 3 and 1?** 4
- **Write the number.**
- **What word tells you to add?** and

Remind children that when one group is put together with another group, the two groups are added together.

Use Exercise 2 for Quick Check.

 Quick Check  **RtI**

Then
If a child misses Exercise 2

Differentiate Instruction with
- RtI Tier 1 Activity, p. 169B
- Reteach 5.1

⚠ **COMMON ERRORS**

Error Children may not understand where to place the numbers.

Example Children write the sum after the word *and*.

Springboard to Learning Explain that the number that goes after *and* tells how many more are added. Point to each number or word as you say, **3 and 1**.

Lesson 5.1 **170**

▶ More Practice

For Exercise 2, read this addition word problem to children. **Two children are playing with the soccer ball. Three children come to them. How many children are playing with the soccer ball now?**

- **How many children are playing with the soccer ball?** 2 **Write the number.**
- **How many children are being added to the group?** 3 **Write the number.**
- **What will you have to do to find how many children there are now?** add; count all of the children
- **What is 2 and 3?** 5 **Write the number.**

H.O.T. Problem Read the following addition word problem.

Two children are sitting on a rug. One more child joins them. How many children are sitting on the rug now?

How can you solve this problem?

Go Deeper

Discuss ways children can solve the problem. Some children may wish to act out the problem while the rest of the class counts each group and solves the problem. Possible answer: I can add 2 and 1. There are three children sitting on the rug now.

Name _____

$$\underline{2} \text{ and } \underline{3}$$

$$\underline{5}$$

DIRECTIONS 2. Listen to the addition word problem. Write the number that shows how many children are playing with the soccer ball. Write the number that shows how many children are being added to the group. Write the number that shows how many children there are now.

Chapter 5 · Lesson 1   one hundred seventy-one **171**

PROBLEM SOLVING REAL WORLD

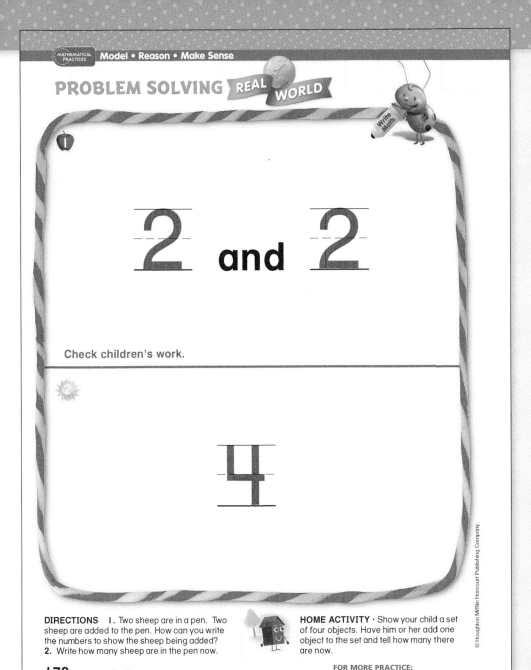

❶

2 and 2

Check children's work.

4

DIRECTIONS **1.** Two sheep are in a pen. Two sheep are added to the pen. How can you write the numbers to show the sheep being added? **2.** Write how many sheep are in the pen now.

172 one hundred seventy-two

 HOME ACTIVITY · Show your child a set of four objects. Have him or her add one object to the set and tell how many there are now.

FOR MORE PRACTICE:
Standards Practice Book, pp. P81–P82

© Houghton Mifflin Harcourt Publishing Company

▶ **Problem Solving**

Have children listen to the addition word problem.

Two sheep are in a pen. Two sheep are added to the pen.

Explain to children that they need to write the numbers that are being added.

• **How many sheep are in the pen?** 2
• **How many sheep are added to the pen?** 2

Some children may wish to draw a simple picture to show their thinking.

For Exercise 2, have children write how many sheep there are in the pen now. 4

 Have children explain how they found how many sheep are in the pen now.

❹ SUMMARIZE

Essential Question

How can you show addition as adding to?
I can count and write how many are in each group. Then I can count and write how many there are now.

Differentiated Instruction — INDEPENDENT ACTIVITIES

Grab-and-Go!
Differentiated Centers Kit

Activities
Get It Together!

Children complete the blue Activity Card 6 by using various objects to make and show different addition combinations.

Literature
Pancakes for All
Children read the book and count the five kittens.

Games
Spin to Add
Children use connecting cubes to model addition problems.

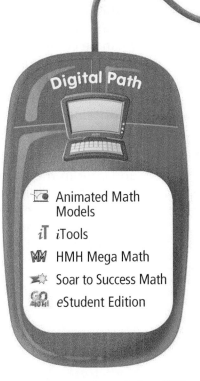

Digital Path

- Animated Math Models
- iTools
- HMH Mega Math
- Soar to Success Math
- eStudent Edition

Hands on •
Addition: Put Together

LESSON AT A GLANCE

Common Core Standard
Understand addition as putting together and adding to, and understand subtraction as taking apart or taking from.
CC.K.OA.1 Represent addition and subtraction with objects, fingers, mental images, drawings, sounds (e.g., claps), acting out situations, verbal explanations, expressions, or equations.

Lesson Objective
Use expressions to represent addition.

Essential Question
How can you show addition as putting together?

Vocabulary
plus

Materials
MathBoard, two-color counters

Digital Path

 eStudent Edition

Daily Routines
Common Core

SPIRAL REVIEW

Problem of the Day

eTransparency
5.2

Number of the Day Tap your foot five times. Clap your hands five times.

Hold up five fingers.

Have children tell what they know about the number 5.

Model Composing Numbers

COMMON CORE
MATHEMATICAL
PRACTICES

In this lesson, children will compose several numbers by placing two-color counters in a ten frame. For example, 7 can be composed with six counters showing the yellow side and one counter showing the red side, or 10 can be composed with two counters showing the yellow side and eight counters showing the red side. These models for composing numbers will give children the background for addition facts, such as 6 + 1 = 7 and 8 + 2 = 10.

In this lesson, children are making models for expressions, and later in the chapter they will be introduced to equations. Children will also find many ways to compose a number in the coming lessons. For example, they will see that 5 can be made from the number pairs: 0 and 5, 1 and 4, 2 and 3, 3 and 2, 4 and 1, and 5 and 0.

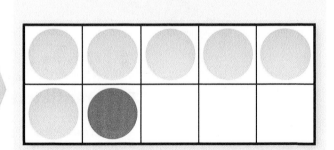

Differentiated Instruction Activities

ELL Language Support
 Visual / Linguistic
Small Group

Strategy: Rephrase

Materials classroom objects

Children can learn new vocabulary by rephrasing a sentence made up of familiar words.

- Put together five red crayons and two blue crayons.

- **I can put together 5 and 2.** Tell children that another way to say this is, **I can add 5 plus 2.** Have children repeat both sentences.

- Put together four orange pencils and four green pencils. **I can put together four orange pencils and four green pencils.** Ask children to tell the same information in another way.

- Repeat with other sets of classroom objects.

See **ELL** Activity Guide for leveled activities.

Enrich
 Kinesthetic
Individual / Partners

Have children draw objects and record their work.

- Have one child fold a sheet of paper in half and draw one to five objects on one side of the paper. Then have the other child draw one to five of the same objects on the other side of the paper.

- Have partners describe what they did. For example: **I drew four cars on my side of the paper. You drew two cars on your side of the paper. Now there are six cars in all.**

- Challenge partners to work together to write the number of objects they drew on the paper in as many different ways as they can using numbers, words, and symbols. Possible answers: 4 + 2, 2 + 4, 6, 4 and 2, 2 and 4

- Have partners take turns choosing the object to draw.

RtI Response to Intervention

Reteach Tier 1
 Kinesthetic / Visual
Whole Class / Small Group

Materials two-color counters, Workmat 3 (ten frame) (see *eTeacher Resources*)

Have children use a ten frame and counters to solve the following problem.

Meg has four yellow counters and two red counters. How many counters does she have in all?

- Have children place four yellow counters in the ten frame.
- Then have them place two red counters in the ten frame.
- **How can you show adding with numbers and a symbol?** 4 + 2
- **How many counters are there in all?** 6 Repeat with other combinations of 10 or less.

Tier 2
 Kinesthetic / Visual
Small Group

Materials two-color counters, Number and Symbol Tiles (front) (see *eTeacher Resources*)

James has four red counters and five yellow counters. How many counters does he have in all?

- **How many red counters does James have?** 4 Have children count four red counters and place the number tile 4 below the set.

- **How many yellow counters does James have?** 5 Have children count five yellow counters and place the number tile 5 below the set.

- **Where do you place the *plus* tile to show the counters put together?** between 4 and 5

- **So, how many counters does James have in all?** 9

 **ENGAGE**

Materials two-color counters

Access Prior Knowledge Make a row of three red counters followed by two yellow counters.

• **How many red counters are in this row?** 3
• **How many yellow counters are in this row?** 2
• **How can you use the word *and* to tell about the counters in this row?** Possible answer: three red counters and two yellow counters

2 TEACH and TALK

▶ **Listen and Draw**

Materials two-color counters

Read this problem aloud as children listen.

Ryan has six yellow counters and one red counter. How many counters does Ryan have in all?

Have children locate the ten frame on the page. Guide them to use yellow and red counters to represent the addition word problem.

• **How many yellow counters are in the ten frame?** 6
• **How many red counters are in the ten frame?** 1
• **You can say the counters show 6 plus 1. Point to *6 plus 1* on the page.**

Explain to children that when they put the set of yellow counters and the set of red counters together, they can use numbers and a plus symbol to show what they did. Point to the plus symbol. Explain that this symbol means to add. It takes the place of the word *and*.

• **You can say 6 and 1 or you can say 6 *plus* 1 when you are adding.**

Explain that when there is a plus symbol, the symbol is read as plus. Guide children to trace the expression. Have them read the expression together. 6 plus 1

• **How many counters does Ryan have in all?** 7 **Write the number.**

 COMMON CORE **CC.K.OA.1** Represent addition and subtraction with objects, fingers, mental images, drawings, sounds (e.g., claps), acting out situations, verbal explanations, expressions, or equations.

Name _____

Addition: Put Together

HANDS ON
Lesson 5.2

Essential Question How can you show addition as putting together?

COMMON CORE STANDARD CC.K.OA.1
Understand addition as putting together and adding to, and understand subtraction as taking apart and taking from.

Listen and Draw

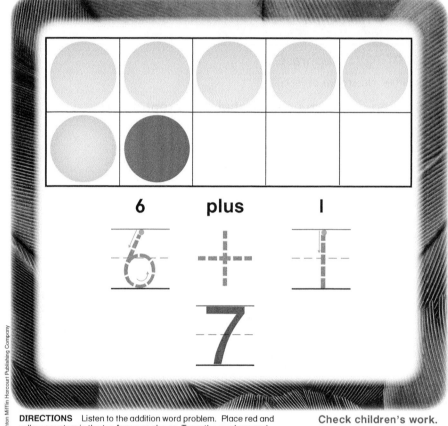

6   plus   1

6 + 1

7

DIRECTIONS Listen to the addition word problem. Place red and yellow counters in the ten frame as shown. Trace the numbers and the symbol to show the sets that are put together. Write the number that shows how many in all.

Check children's work.

Chapter 5 • Lesson 2

one hundred seventy-three **173**

Standards Practice 5.2

Common Core

SPIRAL REVIEW

Name _____

Addition: Put Together

HANDS ON
Lesson 5.2

COMMON CORE STANDARD CC.K.OA.1
Understand addition as putting together and adding to, and understand subtraction as taking apart and taking from.

1

| Y | Y | Y | R | R |
| R | R | R | | |

3   and   5

3 + 5

8

DIRECTIONS Roy has three yellow counters and five red counters. How many counters does he have in all? 1. Place counters in the ten frame to model the sets that are put together. Y is for yellow, and R is for red. Write the numbers and trace the symbol. Write the number to show how many in all.

Chapter 5

eighty-three **P83**

Lesson Check (CC.K.OA.1)

TEST PREP

1

5 + 2   5 + 3   7 + 1   7 + 2
○   ○   ●   ○

Spiral Review (CC.K.CC.2, CC.K.CC.6)

5 6 7 8 ____ 10

6   7   8   9
○   ○   ○   ●

3

5   6   7   9
●   ○   ○   ○

DIRECTIONS 1. Which numbers show the sets that are put together? Mark under your answer. (Lesson 5.2) 2. Count forward. Mark under the number that fills the space. (Lesson 4.4) 3. Meg has seven counters. Paul has a number of counters two less than seven. Mark under the number that shows how many counters Paul has. (Lesson 3.9)

P84 eighty-four

Share and Show

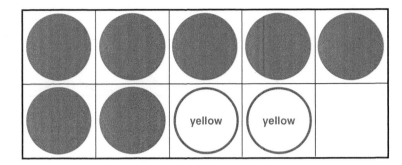

7   plus   2

$$7 + 2$$

$$9$$

DIRECTIONS 1. Listen to the addition word problem. Place red counters in the ten frame as shown. Place yellow counters to model the sets that are put together. Write the numbers and trace the symbol. Write the number to show how many in all.

174 one hundred seventy-four

▶ **Share and Show** • **Guided Practice**

Ask children to listen to the problem.

- Carla has seven red counters and two yellow counters. How many counters does she have in all?
- The ten frame shows Carla's red counters. Place counters on top of the red counters in the ten frame.
- **How many yellow counters does Carla have?** 2

Have children place and draw the yellow counters.

- **How many red counters does Carla have?** 7 **How many yellow counters does she have?** 2
- **You can show this with numbers and words.** Read *7 plus 2* with children.

Explain that this can also be shown with numbers and a symbol.

- **Write the numbers and trace the plus symbol.** 7 + 2
- **Now read the numbers and symbol that tell how many counters Carla has.**
- **How many counters does Carla have in all?** 9 Write the number.

Reteach 5.2

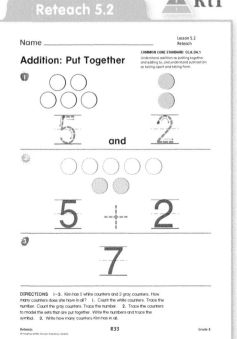

Name _____

Lesson 5.2
Reteach

Addition: Put Together

COMMON CORE STANDARD CC.K.OA.1
Understand addition as putting together and adding to, and understand subtraction as taking apart and taking from.

DIRECTIONS 1–3. Kim has 5 white counters and 2 gray counters. How many counters does she have in all? **1.** Count the white counters. Trace the number. Count the gray counters. Trace the number. **2.** Trace the counters to model the sets that are put together. Write the numbers and trace the symbol. **3.** Write how many counters Kim has in all.

Reteach
© Houghton Mifflin Harcourt Publishing Company   **R33**   Grade K

Enrich 5.2

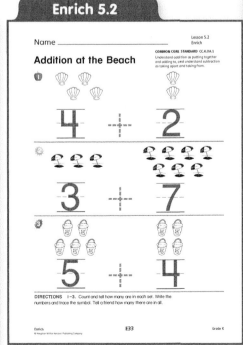

Name _____

Lesson 5.2
Enrich

Addition at the Beach

COMMON CORE STANDARD CC.K.OA.1
Understand addition as putting together and adding to, and understand subtraction as taking apart and taking from.

DIRECTIONS 1–3. Count and tell how many are in each set. Write the numbers and trace the symbol. Tell a friend how many there are in all.

Enrich
© Houghton Mifflin Harcourt Publishing Company   **E33**   Grade K

⚠ COMMON ERRORS

Error Children may count and record the number of counters in each row instead of the number of each color.

Example In Exercise 1, children count and write 5 and 4.

Springboard to Learning Reread the problem and ask if the problem tells about rows of counters or colors of counters. Model how to count how many of each color and record the numbers.

▶ More Practice

For Exercise 2, read this addition word problem.

- **Chas has two yellow counters and eight red counters. How many counters does Chas have in all?** 10

Have children model the problem with counters.

Have children complete the expression and then write how many in all.

Use Exercise 2 for Quick Check.

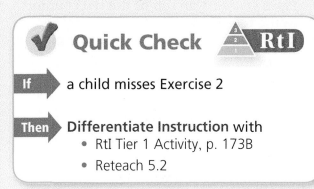

✔ Quick Check

If ▶ a child misses Exercise 2

Then ▶ **Differentiate Instruction** with
- RtI Tier 1 Activity, p. 173B
- Reteach 5.2

H.O.T. Problem Write **3 + 4** on the board. Ask children to describe an addition word problem that matches the expression. Then have them tell how many in all.

Go Deeper

Invite volunteers to share their descriptions with the class and explain why their addition word problems are shown by 3 + 4. By explaining why a problem can be represented by 3 + 4, children show that they understand its meaning.

Name _____

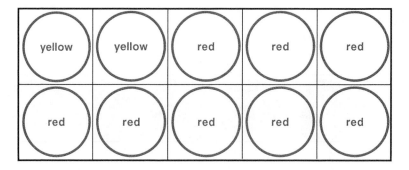

| yellow | yellow | red | red | red |
| red | red | red | red | red |

2   plus   8

$$2 + 8$$
$$10$$

© Houghton Mifflin Harcourt Publishing Company

DIRECTIONS **2.** Listen to the addition word problem. Place counters in the ten frame to model the sets that are put together. How many are there of each color counter? Write the numbers and trace the symbol. Write the number to show how many in all.

Chapter 5 · Lesson 2   one hundred seventy-five **175**

PROBLEM SOLVING REAL WORLD

❶

$$4 + 2$$

Check children's work.

$$6$$

Check children's work.

DIRECTIONS 1. Four red apples and two green apples are on the table. Write the numbers and trace the symbol to show the apples being put together. 2. Write the number to show how many apples in all.

HOME ACTIVITY • Show your child two sets of 4 objects. Have him or her put the sets of objects together and tell how many in all.

176 one hundred seventy-six

FOR MORE PRACTICE:
Standards Practice Book, pp. P83–P84

▶ **Problem Solving**

Have children listen to the problem.

- **Four red apples and two green apples are on the table.**

Discuss what numbers the children need to write to show the apples being put together. 4, 2

- **Write the numbers and trace the symbol.**

Children may wish to draw to show their work.

For Exercise 2, Discuss how they can find how many apples there are in all.

- **Write the number of apples in all.** 6

 After children complete their work, have several children share with the class. Invite them to explain how they know how many apples there are in all.

❹ SUMMARIZE

Essential Question

How can you show addition as putting together? I can count how many objects in each set and write the numbers with a plus symbol between them. Then I can count all of the objects to find how many in all.

Differentiated Instruction — INDEPENDENT ACTIVITIES

Grab-and-Go!
Differentiated Centers Kit

Activities
Get It Together!

Children complete the blue Activity Card 6 by using various objects to make and show different addition combinations.

Literature
Pancakes for All

Children read the book and count the five kittens.

Games
Spin to Add

Children use connecting cubes to model addition problems.

Digital Path

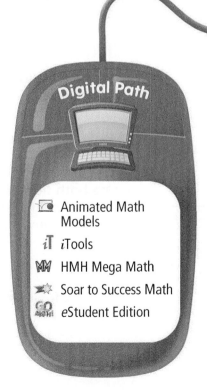

- Animated Math Models
- iTools
- HMH Mega Math
- Soar to Success Math
- eStudent Edition

Problem Solving • Act Out Addition Problems

LESSON AT A GLANCE

Common Core Standard
Understand addition as putting together and adding to, and understand subtraction as taking apart and taking from.
CC.K.OA.1 Represent addition and subtraction with objects, fingers, mental images, drawings, sounds (e.g., claps), acting out situations, verbal explanations, expressions, or equations.

Also CC.K.OA.2, CC.K.OA.5

Lesson Objective
Solve problems by using the strategy *act it out*.

Essential Question
How can you solve problems using the strategy *act it out*?

Vocabulary **is equal to**

Materials
MathBoard

Digital Path

 iTools: Counters   *eStudent Edition*

COMMON CORE
PROFESSIONAL DEVELOPMENT
About the Math

If Children Ask

Have children read the equal symbol as *is equal to*. *Is equal to* means having the same quantity on both sides of the symbol. Thus $2 + 3 = 5$ means $2 + 3$ is the same quantity as 5. Likewise, 5 is the same quantity as $2 + 3$, and $5 = 2 + 3$.

Explain to children that the equation $2 + 3 = 4 + 1$ is true because both sides have the same quantity. The phrase is *the same as* can also be used when you read equations with the children.

 Professional Development Video Podcasts

Daily Routines
Common Core

Problem of the Day   *eTransparency* 5.3

Calendar Math **Today is** _____.

Yesterday was _____.

Tomorrow will be _____.

Locate the date on the calendar and have children read it with you. Use the number of the year.

Vocabulary Builder

Materials connecting cube, Vocabulary Card for *is equal to* (see *eTeacher Resources*)

Is Equal To

Have a volunteer make a four-cube train with yellow cubes. **How many cubes are there?** 4

Have another volunteer make a four-cube train with blue cubes. **How many cubes are there?** 4 **Does each cube train have the same number of cubes?** yes **How can you tell?** I can count them. I see that 4 is the same as 4.

When two numbers are the same, one number is equal to the other number. Make two more cube trains.

Have a volunteer make a three-cube train with yellow cubes. Have another volunteer make a three-cube train with blue cubes. **Is the number of yellow cubes equal to the number of blue cubes?** yes **How do you know?** Both cube trains have three cubes each. **What is another way to say this?** The number of yellow cubes is equal to the number of blue cubes.

Repeat this procedure with other equal numbers of cubes.

Differentiated Instruction Activities

ELL Language Support
Kinesthetic / Visual
Small Group

Strategy: Describe

Materials pattern blocks

Children can practice their comprehension by describing what they have seen or heard.

- Place three blocks on a table. Then add two more blocks to the set.
- Ask children to complete an addition sentence to tell how many blocks.
- Make sure that children say how many blocks there are in all.

Repeat the activity with a different number of pattern blocks.

See ELL Activity Guide for leveled activities.

Enrich
Kinesthetic
Small Group

Have groups of four or five children create their own addition word problems and then act them out.

- Have other children tell the answer to each group's addition word problems.
- Ask groups to illustrate their problems and write how many.

RtI Response to Intervention

Reteach Tier 1
Visual / Kinesthetic
Whole Class / Small Group

Materials crayons

Use crayons or other classroom objects to demonstrate addition word problems.

- Put three crayons on the table. **How many crayons are on the table?** 3
- Hold two crayons in your hand. **How many crayons are in my hand?** 2
- Add the two crayons in your hand to the crayons on the table.
- Provide children with an addition sentence to complete. **How many crayons are on the table now?** 5
- Have children show with their fingers the total number of crayons on the table.

Repeat with other examples.

Tier 2
Visual / Kinesthetic
Small Group

Tell children the following addition word problem.

There were three bears in the forest eating berries. Two more bears came into the forest to eat berries with them.

- Tell the children that they are going to model the addition problem. Ask for three volunteers to come to the "forest" in the front of the class and pretend they are bears eating berries.
- **How can you show that two more bears came to them in the forest?** Possible answer: Two children can pretend they are bears walking into the forest. **Have children act out the problem. Provide children with an addition sentence to complete.**
- **How many bears are in the forest now?** 5

Repeat with other examples.

1 ENGAGE

Access Prior Knowledge Remind children that they have previously used models to solve problems. Tell them that, in this lesson, they are going to use the strategy *act it out* to solve the problems.

- **Have you ever been playing on your own and then a friend comes to play with you?**
- **How many children will you need to act this out?** 2

Let children share other experiences that they could act out.

2 TEACH and TALK iTools Online

▶ **Unlock the Problem** MATHEMATICAL PRACTICES

Read this addition word problem aloud as children listen.

Two children are painting. Two more children come to paint. How many children are there now?

Ask children what they need to find to solve the problem. how many children in all

- **How many children are already painting at the easel?** 2
- **How many more children are coming to paint?** 2
- **How can you find out how many children there are in all?** I can count all of the children.
- **How many children are there in all?** 4; there are two children at the easel; two more children walk to them.

Ask children to point to the *is equal to* symbol.

This is the *is equal to* symbol. It means *is the same as*. The quantity on one side of the symbol is the same as the quantity on the other side of the symbol.

Point to and define *addition sentence*. Explain that it has a *plus* symbol and an *is equal to* symbol.

- **What is on one side of the *is equal to* symbol?** 2 + 2 **What is on the other side?** 4
- **What does 2 + 2 tell you?** there are two children and two more come
- **What does 4 tell you?** how many children in all
- **What is 2 + 2 the same as?** 4
- **How can you say the addition sentence?** 2 plus 2 is equal to 4; 2 plus 2 is the same as 4 **Trace the addition sentence.**

MATHEMATICAL PRACTICES **What happens when two quantities are combined?**

177 Chapter 5

COMMON CORE

CC.K.OA.1 Represent addition and subtraction with objects, fingers, mental images, drawings, sounds (e.g., claps), acting out situations, verbal explanations, expressions, or equations.

Name _____

Problem Solving • Act Out Addition Problems

PROBLEM SOLVING
Lesson 5.3

COMMON CORE STANDARD CC.K.OA.1

Understand addition as putting together and adding to, and understand subtraction as taking apart and taking from.

Essential Question How can you solve problems using the strategy *act it out*?

🔑 **Unlock the Problem** REAL WORLD

DIRECTIONS Listen to and act out the addition word problem. Trace the addition sentence. Tell a friend how many children in all.

Check children's work.

Chapter 5 • Lesson 3

one hundred seventy-seven **177**

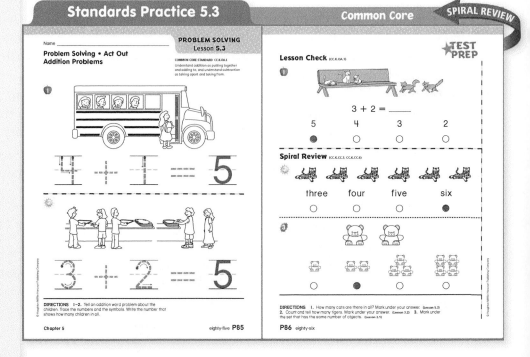

Standards Practice 5.3

Common Core SPIRAL REVIEW

Name _____

Problem Solving • Act Out Addition Problems

PROBLEM SOLVING
Lesson 5.3

COMMON CORE STANDARD CC.K.OA.1
Understand addition as putting together and adding to, and understand subtraction as taking apart and taking from.

DIRECTIONS 1–2. Tell an addition word problem about the children. Trace the numbers and the symbols. Write the number that shows how many children in all.

Chapter 5

eighty-five **P85**

Lesson Check (CC.K.OA.1)

★ **TEST PREP**

3 + 2 = _____

5   4   3   2
●   ○   ○   ○

Spiral Review (CC.K.CC.3, CC.K.CC.6)

three   four   five   six
○   ○   ○   ●

DIRECTIONS 1. How many cats are there in all? Mark under your answer. (Lesson 5.3) **2.** Count and tell how many tigers. Mark under your answer. (Lesson 3.2) **3.** Mark under the set that has the same number of objects. (Lesson 3.1)

P86 eighty-six

Try Another Problem

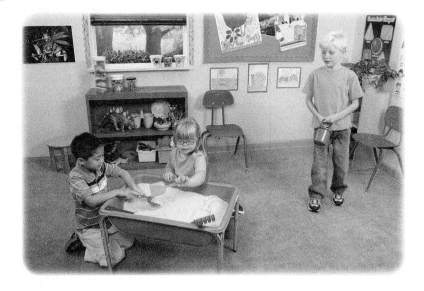

••••••••••••••••••••••••••••••••••••••

DIRECTIONS I. Listen to and act out the addition word problem. Trace the numbers and the symbols. Write the number that shows how many children in all.

178 one hundred seventy-eight

Ask children to listen and invite volunteers to act out the addition word problem for Exercise 1.

* **There are two children playing at a sand table. Then one more child comes to play with them.**
* **How many children are at the sand table?** 2
* **How many more children come to play with them?** 1
* **How many children are at the sand table now?** 3
* **Trace the numbers and the symbols. Write how many in all.**
* **How would you say the addition sentence?** 2 + 1 is equal to 3; 2 plus 1 is the same as 3
* **How does the addition sentence tell about the children in the picture?** 2 tells the number of children at the sand table. 1 tells the number of children that come to play. 3 tells how many children in all.
* **What does the plus symbol tell you?** It tells me to add the number of children at the sand table and the number of children that come to play.
* **What does the *is equal to* symbol tell you?** It tells me that 2 + 1 is the same as 3.

Use Exercise 2 for **Quick Check**.

 Quick Check  RtI

If a child misses Exercise 2

Then **Differentiate Instruction with**
* RtI Tier 1 Activity, p. 177B
* Reteach 5.3
* Soar to Success Math 10.03

! **COMMON ERRORS**

Error Children may count only one group of children.

Example Children count only the children at the sand table in Exercise 1.

Springboard to Learning Explain that to find how many children there are now, all the children from both groups need to be counted. Model counting each child as children count along with you.

Reteach 5.3 RtI

Name _____ Lesson 5.3 Reteach

COMMON CORE STANDARD CC.K.OA.1
Understand addition as putting together and adding to, and understand subtraction as taking apart and taking from.

Problem Solving • Act Out Addition Problems

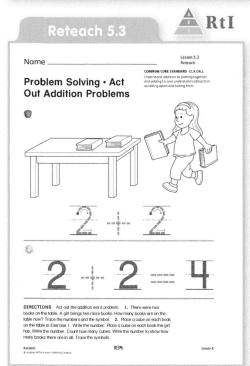

DIRECTIONS Act out the addition word problem. I. There were two books on the table. A girl brings two more books. How many books are on the table now? Trace the numbers and the symbol. 2. Place a cube on each book on the table in Exercise 1. Write the number. Place a cube on each book the girl has. Write the number. Count how many cubes. Write the number to show how many books there are in all. Trace the symbols.

Reteach   R34   Grade K
© Houghton Mifflin Harcourt Publishing Company

Enrich 5.3

Name _____ Lesson 5.3 Enrich

COMMON CORE STANDARD CC.K.OA.1
Understand addition as putting together and adding to, and understand subtraction as taking apart and taking from.

Fish Addition

2 + 3 = 5

4 + 1 = 5

DIRECTIONS 1–2. Count and write how many fish are in each set. Tell and write how many in all.

Enrich   E34   Grade K
© Houghton Mifflin Harcourt Publishing Company

(3) PRACTICE

▶ **Share and Show** • Guided Practice

Focus attention on the children in the picture in Exercise 2. Then read the following problem and have children act it out.

- **There are three children at the table. Then two more children come to the table.**
- **How many children are at the table?** 3
- **How many more children come to the table?** 2
- **Trace the numbers and the symbols.**
- **How many children are at the table now?** 5 **Write the number.**

H.O.T. Problem In Exercise 2, one child is wearing a green shirt. Suppose two more children wearing green shirts come to the table. Now how many children at the table are wearing green shirts?

Go Deeper

To solve the H.O.T. Problem, children start counting a child who is in the picture and then add children who are not visible to count. Have them complete an addition sentence and solve the problem. 1 + 2 = 3 Children may act out the addition word problem to check.

Name _____

Share and Show

$$3 + 2 = 5$$

DIRECTIONS 2. Listen to and act out the addition word problem. Trace the numbers and the symbols. Write the number that shows how many children in all.

Chapter 5 • Lesson 3

one hundred seventy-nine **179**

COMMON CORE PROFESSIONAL DEVELOPMENT

Mathematical Practices in Your Classroom

CC.K–12.MP.4 Model with mathematics.

Being able to apply mathematics to solve everyday problems is an important part of mathematics.

- Children are able to solve problems in class and learn how to apply that knowledge to situations that occur in their everyday life.
- When children are able to model an addition problem to describe a situation they encounter in everyday life, it provides a sample, demonstrating that they have a true understanding of how to apply what they have learned. This shows they not only can solve a given problem, but can take a situation and turn it into a mathematical problem, applying the strategies learned to solve it.

There are three plates on the table. Mom puts one more plate on the table. How many plates are on the table now?

- **How can you solve the problem?** I can start with 3 and add one more. When I add one more it will be the next counting number. Four comes right after 3.
- **Does your answer make sense?** Yes, because I started with 3 and added one more. I know 4 is one more than 3.

179 Chapter 5

On Your Own REAL WORLD

1

$$3 + 1 = 4$$

$$1 + 4 = 5$$

Check children's work.

DIRECTIONS **1.** Tell an addition word problem about the puppies. Trace the numbers and the symbols. Write the number that shows how many puppies there are now. **2.** Draw a picture to match this addition sentence. Write how many in all. Tell a friend about your drawing.

HOME ACTIVITY • Tell your child a short word problem about adding three objects to a set of two objects. Have your child use toys to act out the word problem.

180 one hundred eighty

FOR EXTRA PRACTICE: Standards Practice Book, p. P105

FOR MORE PRACTICE: Standards Practice Book, pp. P85–P86

© Houghton Mifflin Harcourt Publishing Company

▶ On Your Own

Ask children to look at the puppies at the top of the page. Have them explain how they will solve the addition word problem to find how many puppies there are now.

- **How many puppies are in each set?** 3 and 1

Call on a volunteer to create an addition word problem to go with the picture.

- **Trace the numbers and the symbols.**
- **How many puppies are there now?** 4 Write the number.

For Exercise 2, tell children to draw a picture to match the addition sentence, $1 + 4 = $ _____. Then have them trace the numbers and symbols and write how many in all. Invite several children to share and discuss their drawings. Children should demonstrate an understanding of adding sets in both their art and words.

You may suggest that children place the completed On Your Own page in their portfolios.

4 SUMMARIZE

Essential Question

How can you solve problems using the strategy *act it out*? I can act out an addition word problem. I can count the people or objects in both sets to find how many in all.

Differentiated Instruction — INDEPENDENT ACTIVITIES

Grab-and-Go!
Differentiated Centers Kit

Activities
Come Together!

Children complete the orange Activity Card 6 by using counters and number tiles to show addition combinations.

Literature
Flowers for Flossie

Children read the book and count and add flowers of different colors.

Games
Spin to Add

Children use connecting cubes to model addition problems.

Digital Path

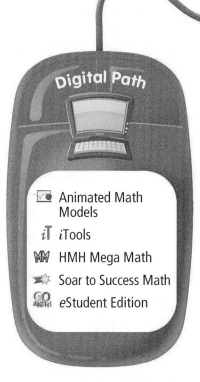

- Animated Math Models
- iTools
- HMH Mega Math
- Soar to Success Math
- eStudent Edition

Lesson 5.3 **180**

Hands On: Algebra • Model and Draw Addition Problems

LESSON AT A GLANCE

Common Core Standard
Understand addition as putting together and adding to, and understand subtraction as taking apart and taking from.
CC.K.OA.5 Fluently add and subtract within 5.

Also CC.K.OA.1, CC.K.OA.2

Lesson Objective
Use objects and drawings to solve addition word problems within 5.

Essential Question
How can you use objects and drawings to solve addition word problems?

Materials
MathBoard, connecting cubes

Digital Path

☑ Animated Math Models

📱 iTools: Counters

〰 HMH Mega Math

🔵 eStudent Edition

**COMMON CORE
PROFESSIONAL
DEVELOPMENT**

About the Math

Teaching for Depth

In this lesson, children physically put together cubes to model addition. This action lets them show addition in a very concrete way. As children work, you can ask the question, "How many do we have in all?" You may also want to rephrase the questions with different words by asking, "How many all together?" or "What is the total number?" You could even introduce the term *sum* when speaking of the answer to an addition word problem.

Some children will be able to anticipate the sum even before putting together the connecting cubes. Several times during the lesson, you might ask children to predict the sum and then verify it by counting the cubes after they are put together.

As they put together cubes, summarize what children have done: "We had cube trains of two cubes and three cubes. We put them together and had five cubes in all."

 Professional Development Video Podcasts

Daily Routines 📋 Math Board

Common Core

SPIRAL REVIEW

Problem of the Day
eTransparency **5.4**

Number of the Day Hold up one red cube and one blue cube. How many red cubes are shown? How many blue cubes? How many cubes in all? 1; 1; 2

Have children make cube trains of three cubes and two cubes. Have them put together the cube trains. Repeat with one and four.

Vocabulary Builder

Materials Numeral Cards (0–7) (see *eTeacher Resources*)

One Greater

Show the numeral cards one at a time. Have children read each number, and then name the number that is one greater.

- **Show children numeral card 7. What number is this?** 7

Have children point to the numeral card that is one greater.

- **What number is one greater than 7?** 8

Continue until children have identified all the numbers and have named one greater than each.

7   8

Differentiated Instruction Activities

ELL Language Support
 Verbal / Linguistic
Small Group

Strategy: Model Language

Children can learn correct pronunciation and sentence structure by repeating words and sentences that are modeled by a native speaker.

- Have children repeat each sentence as you read the following addition word problem. **Two blue chairs and one yellow chair are in the kitchen. How many chairs are in the kitchen?**

- Draw the chairs on the board as you tell the problem again.

- Write an addition sentence on the board. Have children tell the numbers as you write, **2 + 1 = 3.**

- **How many chairs are in the kitchen?** 3

See ELL Activity Guide for leveled activities.

Enrich
 Kinesthetic
Partners

Materials magazines, scissors, glue, drawing paper, connecting cubes

Have partners find and cut out a picture from a magazine that shows one to four people, animals, or objects being put together. Have them glue the picture onto a sheet of paper.

- Then have one child create an addition word problem about the picture. Have the partner model with connecting cubes.

- Then have partners write numbers to complete an addition sentence to show how many are put together and how many in all.

RtI Response to Intervention

Reteach Tier 1
 Visual / Kinesthetic
Whole Class / Small Group

Materials Numeral Cards (0–7) (see *eTeacher Resources*)

Tell children the following addition word problem: **One bear is splashing in the river. Three bears are swimming in the river. How many bears are in the river?**

- Tell children they are going to tell this addition word problem with their fingers. Have them pretend that each of their fingers is a bear. Tell the problem again and have the children model it with their fingers.

- **How many bears are splashing?** 1 **How many bears are swimming?** 3 **How many bears are there in all?** 4

- **How can you use numbers to complete an addition sentence for this problem?** 1 + 3 = 4

Tier 2
 Visual / Kinesthetic
Small Group

Materials two-color counters

Give children the following addition word problem: **Jan has three balls. Her friend has two balls. How many balls do they have?**

- **Show this problem with counters. How many counters would you use to show the number of balls that Jan has?** 3

- **How many more counters would you use to show the number of balls Jan's friend has?** 2

- **How many counters are there in all?** 5 **How can you complete an addition sentence for this problem?** 3 + 2 = 5

Repeat with other examples.

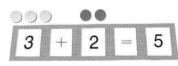

1 ENGAGE

Access Prior Knowledge Have you ever had other children added to your group when you were doing something? yes

Let children share experiences.

- **After children were added to your group, did you have more children, or fewer children doing the activity?** more children

Lead a class discussion of other times more may have been added to something, such as birds on a lawn or dishes on a table.

2 TEACH and TALK GO Online Animated Math Models

▶ **Listen and Draw**

Materials connecting cubes

Read aloud this addition word problem as children listen.

Rita has one red cube and one blue cube. How many cubes does Rita have?

Give each child one red cube and one blue cube. Help children locate the red and blue cubes on the top of the page.

- **Use your cubes to cover the cubes on the top of the page.**
- **How many red cubes are there?** 1
- **How many blue cubes are there?** 1
- **Put the red and blue cubes together to make a cube train.**
- **Color to show how the cube train looks.**
- **Count the cubes. How many cubes are there in the cube train?** 2

Remind children that the *is equal to* symbol in the addition sentence means *is the same as*. It can be read as *is equal to*.

- **Trace the addition sentence. It also tells how many cubes are put together.**
- **How would you read the addition sentence?**
  1 plus 1 is equal to 2.

Reread the problem. Have children use their cubes and the addition sentence to solve.

- **How many cubes does Rita have?** 2

CC.K.OA.5 Fluently add and subtract within 5.

Name _____

Algebra • Model and Draw Addition Problems

HANDS ON Lesson 5.4

COMMON CORE STANDARD CC.K.OA.5
Understand addition as putting together and adding to, and understand subtraction as taking apart and taking from.

Essential Question How can you use objects and drawings to solve addition word problems?

Listen and Draw

$$1 + 1 = 2$$

DIRECTIONS Place cubes as shown. Listen to the addition word problem. Model to show the cubes put together in a cube train. Color to show how the cube train looks. Trace to complete the addition sentence.

Chapter 5 • Lesson 4

Check children's work.

one hundred eighty-one **181**

Standards Practice 5.4

Common Core

SPIRAL REVIEW

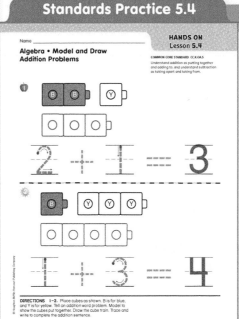

Name _____

Algebra • Model and Draw Addition Problems

HANDS ON Lesson 5.4

COMMON CORE STANDARD CC.K.OA.5
Understand addition as putting together and adding to, and understand subtraction as taking apart and taking from.

$$2 + 1 = 3$$

$$1 + 3 = 4$$

DIRECTIONS 1–2. Place cubes as shown. B is for blue, and Y is for yellow. Tell an addition word problem. Model to show the cubes put together. Draw the cube train. Trace and write to complete the addition sentence.

Chapter 5

eighty-seven **P87**

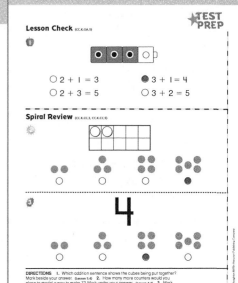

Lesson Check (CC.K.OA.5)

⃝ 2 + 1 = 3   ● 3 + 1 = 4
⃝ 2 + 3 = 5   ⃝ 3 + 2 = 5

Spiral Review (CC.K.CC.3, CC.K.CC.5)

4

DIRECTIONS 1. Which addition sentence shows the cubes being put together? Mark beside your answer. (Lesson 5.4) 2. How many more counters would you place to model a way to make 7? Mark under your answer. (Lesson 3.3) 3. Mark under the set that shows the number. (Lesson 1.4)

P88 eighty-eight

Share and Show

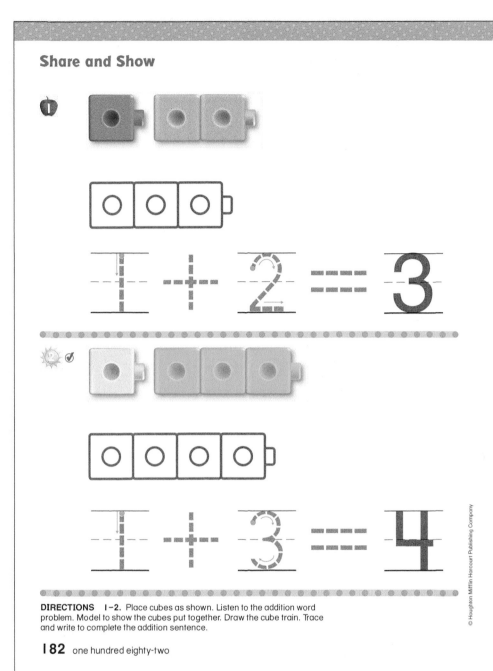

1

$$1 + 2 = 3$$

$$1 + 3 = 4$$

DIRECTIONS 1-2. Place cubes as shown. Listen to the addition word problem. Model to show the cubes put together. Draw the cube train. Trace and write to complete the addition sentence.

182 one hundred eighty-two

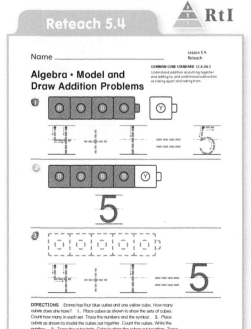

Reteach 5.4 ▲ RtI

Name _____

Lesson 5.4
Reteach

Algebra • Model and Draw Addition Problems

COMMON CORE STANDARD CC.K.OA.5
Understand addition as putting together and adding to, and understand subtraction as taking apart and taking from.

DIRECTIONS Emma has four blue cubes and one yellow cube. How many cubes does she have? 1. Place cubes as shown to show the sets of cubes. Count how many in each set. Trace the numbers and the symbol. 2. Place cubes as shown to model the cubes put together. Count the cubes. Write the number. 3. Trace the cube train. Color to show the cubes put together. Trace and write to complete the addition sentence.

Reteach R35 Grade K

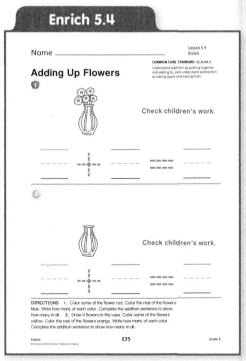

Enrich 5.4

Name _____

Lesson 5.4
Enrich

Adding Up Flowers

COMMON CORE STANDARD CC.K.OA.5
Understand addition as putting together and adding to, and understand subtraction as taking apart and taking from.

Check children's work.

Check children's work.

DIRECTIONS 1. Color some of the flower red. Color the rest of the flowers blue. Write how many of each color. Complete the addition sentence to show how many in all. 2. Draw 4 flowers in the vase. Color some of the flowers yellow. Color the rest of the flowers orange. Write how many of each color. Complete the addition sentence to show how many in all.

Enrich E35 Grade K

---

3 **PRACTICE**

▶ **Share and Show • Guided Practice**

Work through Exercise 1 with children. Ask children to listen to the addition word problem and model it by placing connecting cubes as shown.

- **Abby has one blue cube. She has two orange cubes. How many cubes does she have?**
- **Place one blue cube and two orange cubes on top of the ones shown.**
- **How many blue cubes are there?** 1 **How many orange cubes are there?** 2 **Put the cubes together. Draw the cube train.**
- **To find how many cubes Abby has, you can count the cubes. How many cubes are there?** 3
- **Trace and write to complete the addition sentence. How many cubes are in the cube train?** 3

For Exercise 2, ask children to listen to the addition word problem and model it with cubes. Have them draw the cube train, count the cubes, and trace and write to complete the addition sentence.

- **Eva has one yellow cube and three green cubes. How many cubes does Eva have?** 4

Use Exercise 2 for Quick Check.

 Quick Check

If a child misses Exercise 2

Then Differentiate Instruction with
- RtI Tier 1 Activity, p. 181B
- Reteach 5.4
- Soar to Success Math 10.03

 COMMON ERRORS

Error After putting together cubes, children may write one of the addends as the sum.

Example Children put together 1 and 3 and write 3 as the sum in Exercise 2.

Springboard to Learning Model counting each cube before putting them together, emphasize putting them together, and then have children touch and count all the cubes on the cube train one at a time.

▶ More Practice

Explain that this page will be done the same as the previous page.

- Lilly has four red cubes and one yellow cube. How many cubes does she have? 5
- Tom has one blue cube and four green cubes. How many cubes does he have? 5

H.O.T. Problem Eli has three orange cubes and two yellow cubes. How many cubes does he have?

Go Deeper

Have children build one three-cube train and one two-cube train. Then have them put together the two cube trains and tell how many cubes in all. 5 Discuss ways children might go about solving the problem, including solving without cubes.

4 SUMMARIZE

Essential Question

How can you use objects and drawings to solve addition word problems? I can show how many are in each set and then put them together. I can complete the addition sentence to match what I did with the objects using numbers and symbols.

Name _____

③

④

DIRECTIONS 3–4. Place cubes as shown. Listen to the addition word problem. Model to show the cubes put together. Draw the cube train. Trace and write to complete the addition sentence.

HOME ACTIVITY · Tell your child a short word problem about adding two objects to a set of another two objects. Have him or her use objects to model the word problem.

Chapter 5 · Lesson 4 **FOR MORE PRACTICE:** Standards Practice Book, pp. P87–P88 one hundred eighty-three **183**

© Houghton Mifflin Harcourt Publishing Company

Differentiated Instruction · INDEPENDENT ACTIVITIES

Grab-and-Go!
Differentiated Centers Kit

Activities
Get It Together!

Children complete the blue Activity Card 6 by using various objects to make and show different addition combinations.

Literature
Pancakes for All

Children read the book and count the five kittens.

Games
Spin to Add

Children use connecting cubes to model addition problems.

Digital Path

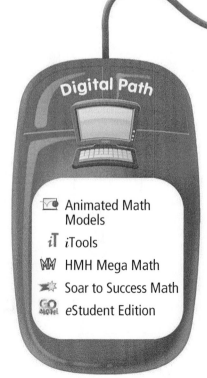

- Animated Math Models
- iTools
- HMH Mega Math
- Soar to Success Math
- eStudent Edition

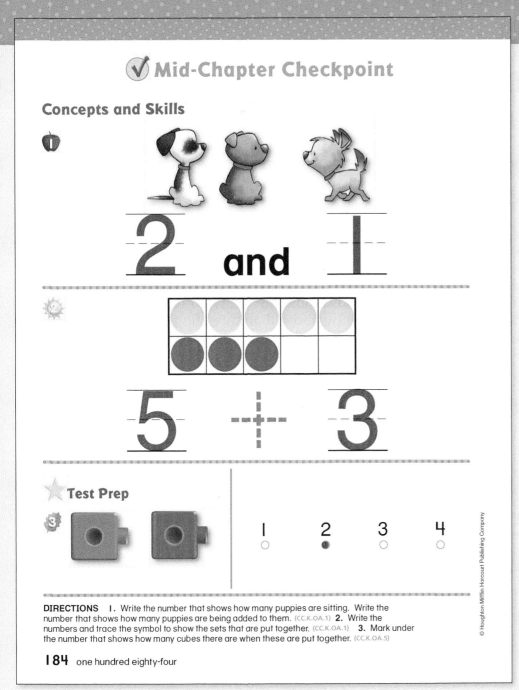

✓ Mid-Chapter Checkpoint

Concepts and Skills

1.

2 and 1

2.

5 + 3

⭐ Test Prep

3.

| 1 | 2 | 3 | 4 |

© Houghton Mifflin Harcourt Publishing Company

DIRECTIONS 1. Write the number that shows how many puppies are sitting. Write the number that shows how many puppies are being added to them. (CC.K.OA.1) **2.** Write the numbers and trace the symbol to show the sets that are put together. (CC.K.OA.1) **3.** Mark under the number that shows how many cubes there are when these are put together. (CC.K.OA.5)

184 one hundred eighty-four

Formative Assessment

Use the **Mid-Chapter Checkpoint** to assess children's learning and progress in the first half of the chapter. The formative assessment provides the opportunity to adjust teaching methods for individual or whole class instruction.

✓ Data-Driven Decision Making 🔺 RtI

Based on the results of the Mid-Chapter Checkpoint, use the following resources to strengthen individual or whole class instruction.

Item	Lesson	*CCSS	Common Error	Intervene With	Soar to Success Math
1	5.1	CC.K.OA.1	May write incorrect numbers for the sets	R—5.1; TE—p. 169B	
2	5.2	CC.K.OA.1	May write incorrect numbers for the sets	R—5.2; TE—p. 173B	
3	5.4	CC.K.OA.5	May add incorrectly	R—5.4; TE—p. 181B	10.03

***CCSS**—Common Core State Standards   **Key: R**—Reteach Book; **TE**—RtI Activities

Algebra • Write Addition Sentences for 10

LESSON AT A GLANCE

Common Core Standard

Understand addition as putting together and adding to, and understand subtraction as taking apart and taking from.

CC.K.OA.4 For any number from 1 to 9, find the number that makes 10 when added to the given number, e.g., by using objects or drawings, and record the answer with a drawing or equation.

Also CC.K.OA.1, CC.K.OA.2

Lesson Objective

Use a drawing to find 10 from a given number and record the equation.

Essential Question

How can you use a drawing to find the number that makes a ten from a given number?

Materials

MathBoard

Digital Path

- ☑ Animated Math Models
- ⅈT *iTools:* Counters
- ⋈ HMH Mega Math
- eStudent Edition

COMMON CORE PROFESSIONAL DEVELOPMENT

About the Math

Teaching for Depth

Many different situations involve addition. In this lesson, children will be working with situations that involve putting together with an unknown addend. An example of this would be: There are five children. Four are wearing shorts. The rest are wearing jeans. How many children are wearing jeans?

Children will need help as they learn to recognize which part needs to be found. Some children often see a plus symbol and add the numbers given in the problem. In this example, they might add 5 and 4. Take time to walk the children through these problems, step by step, pointing out that the number being added is the unknown number and that they have been given the number that tells how many in all, or the total.

Professional Development Video Podcasts

Daily Routines
Common Core

SPIRAL REVIEW

Problem of the Day

eTransparency **5.5**

Number of the Day Hold up three fingers. Now show fewer than three fingers. Now show more than three fingers.

three fingers; zero, one, or two fingers; four or more fingers

Repeat the activity starting with another number.

Fluency Builder

Counting Tape

Materials Counting Tape

Continue to update daily, and to look at number neighbors, and to count on and back. Encourage children to share their ideas with each other, both by speaking and by listening.

- **What are the number neighbors for 73?**
- **How many squares have you put up since Day 70?**
- **How many more days are there until Day 75? Until Day 80?**
- **How did you decide that?**

Return occasionally to discuss the numbers from earlier in the year so that all children can participate.

- **What are the number neighbors for 10?**
- **How much is 10 squares and 3 more?**
- **How much is 20 squares and 3 more?**

| 67 | 68 | 69 | 70 | 71 | 72 | 73 | 74 | 75 |

Differentiated Instruction Activities

ELL Language Support
 Kinesthetic
Small Group

Strategy: Draw

Materials crayons

Children can demonstrate their prior knowledge and understanding by drawing rather than by using language.

- **There are ten cubes. Three cubes are green. The rest are blue. How many blue cubes are there?**

- Elicit from children that the number of blue cubes is not known. Tell children to draw the three green cubes and then as many blue cubes as they need to have ten cubes in all. 7

- Have children say, "Now we know there are seven blue cubes."

- Repeat with other combinations of green and blue cubes that make ten cubes in all.

See **ELL** Activity Guide for leveled activities.

Enrich
 Kinesthetic
Individual / Partners

Materials two-color counters, crayons

Have children use two-color counters and then draw to solve the following problem.

Rita spills out ten counters. Seven are red. The rest are yellow. How many counters are yellow?

- Have children write the numbers to complete an addition sentence that shows the information they are given and the place where the number is unknown. 7 + __ = 10 Then have them make a drawing to represent the word problem and the solution. 3

- Have children compare their answers.

- Challenge children to make up a similar problem in which there are ten in all. Have them tell the problem to their partners to solve.

RtI Response to Intervention

Reteach Tier 1
 Kinesthetic / Visual
Whole Class / Small Group

Materials connecting cubes

Michael has ten cubes. Four are red and the rest are yellow. How many yellow cubes does he have?

- Write the format for an addition sentence on the board. Show the second addend as unknown, **4 + _____ = 10.**

- Ask children to act out the problem with cubes. Then have them complete the addition sentence. 6

- Repeat with other combinations of red and yellow cubes that make ten cubes in all. You might ask children to make up a problem for each set of cubes you give them to make ten in all.

Tier 2
 Visual / Kinesthetic
Small Group

Materials two-color counters, Workmat 3 (ten frame) (see *eTeacher Resources*)

Put three red counters in a ten frame.

- **How many red counters are in the ten frame?** 3

- **How many yellow counters do you need to fill the rest of the ten frame?** 7

- Have children fill in the ten frame with yellow counters. **How many counters did you use?** 7

- Have children use the information they know: the ten spaces in the ten frame and the three red counters. Guide them to write these numbers to complete an addition sentence.

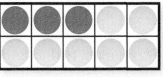

3 + 7 = 10

1 ENGAGE

GO Online · *i*Tools

Materials *i*Tools: Counters

Access Prior Knowledge Show a row of two red and three yellow counters. Ask how many red counters and how many yellow counters there are. 2; 3

- **What addition sentence tells about the counters?** 2 + 3 = 5

Continue with other numbers of red and yellow counters (up to a total of five counters).

2 TEACH and TALK

GO Online · Animated Math Models

▶ **Listen and Draw**

Read aloud this problem as children listen:

Sam made a cube train with ten cubes. Nine are red cubes, and the rest are blue. How many cubes are blue?

Have children look at the cube train.

- **How many red cubes do you see?** 9
- **How many blue cubes do you need to add to make 10?** 1 **Trace the blue cube.**

Have children look at the addition sentence at the bottom of the page.

- **What does the number 9 tell you about the cube train?** the number of red cubes in the cube train
- **What does the number 10 tell you about the cube train?** the number of all of the cubes in the cube train
- **What number is unknown or missing in the word problem?** the number of blue cubes in the cube train
- **What number do you need to find?** the number of blue cubes in the cube train
- **How many blue cubes do you need to add to make 10?** 1
- **What is the unknown or missing number? How do you know?** 1; there is one blue cube in the cube train.

Have children trace the addition sentence.

Read the addition sentence together. **9 plus 1 is equal to 10.**

Reread the problem and review that there were ten cubes in all and nine of them were red. Children had to find how many were added to 9 to make 10 to find the number of blue cubes.

CC.K.OA.4 For any number from 1 to 9, find the number that makes 10 when added to the given number, e.g., by using objects or drawings, and record the answer with a drawing or equation.

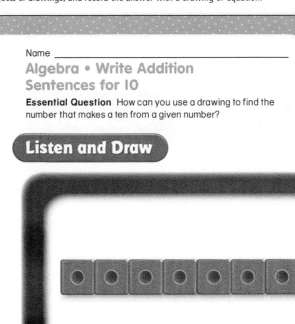

Name _____

Lesson 5.5

Algebra • Write Addition Sentences for 10

COMMON CORE STANDARD CC.K.OA.4
Understand addition as putting together and adding to, and understand subtraction as taking apart and taking from.

Essential Question How can you use a drawing to find the number that makes a ten from a given number?

> **Listen and Draw**

$$9 + 1 = 10$$

© Houghton Mifflin Harcourt Publishing Company

DIRECTIONS Look at the cube train. How many red cubes do you see? How many blue cubes do you need to add to make 10? Trace the blue cube. Trace to show this as an addition sentence.

Check children's work.

Chapter 5 · Lesson 5

one hundred eighty-five **185**

Standards Practice 5.5

Common Core

SPIRAL REVIEW

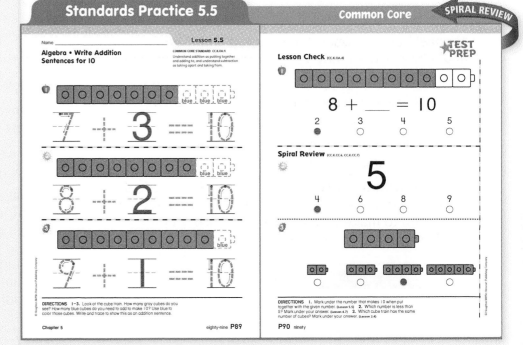

Share and Show

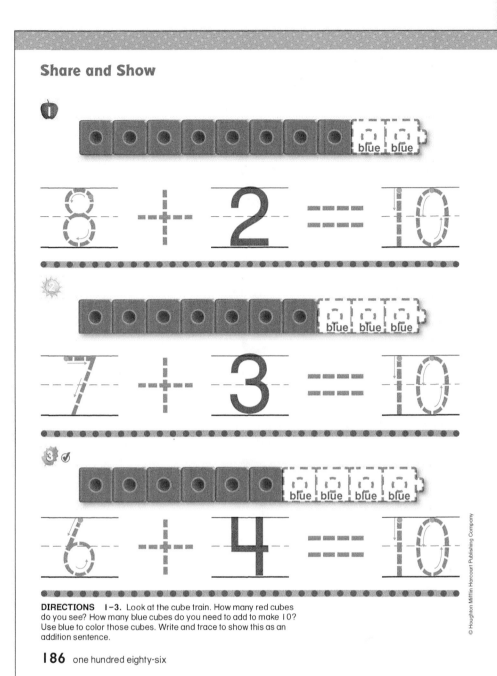

①

$$8 + 2 = 10$$

② blue blue blue

$$7 + 3 = 10$$

③ ✓ blue blue blue blue

$$6 + 4 = 10$$

DIRECTIONS 1–3. Look at the cube train. How many red cubes do you see? How many blue cubes do you need to add to make 10? Use blue to color those cubes. Write and trace to show this as an addition sentence.

186 one hundred eighty-six

© Houghton Mifflin Harcourt Publishing Company

---

③ **PRACTICE** Math Board

▶ **Share and Show • Guided Practice**

Work through Exercise 1 with children to help them understand that they are finding the unknown or missing number that when added to the given number is equal to 10 in all.

- **How many red cubes do you see?** 8
- **How many blue cubes do you need to add to make 10?**

Have children trace and color blue cubes one at a time until the cube train has 10 in all.

- **How many blue cubes did you need?** 2

Guide children to write the number.

Then have them write and trace to show this as an addition sentence.

Use similar questioning for Exercises 2 and 3.

Use Exercise 3 for **Quick Check.**

✓ **Quick Check** ▲ RtI

If ➤ a child misses Exercise 3

Then ➤ Differentiate Instruction with
- RtI Tier 1 Activity, p. 185B
- Reteach 5.5

⚠ **COMMON ERRORS**

Error Children may add the given addend and the sum.

Example In Exercise 3, children write 16.

Springboard to Learning Explain that the number after the *is equal to* symbol is the number that shows both sets of cubes put together, so it is not added.

► More Practice

Have children look at Exercise 4.

- **How many red cubes do you see?** 5
- **How many blue cubes do you need to add to make 10?** 5

Have children draw the cubes. Then have them write and trace to show this as an addition sentence.

For Exercises 5 through 6, read the directions to children. If it is helpful, provide short addition word problems about cube trains and work through the problems step by step with children.

H.O.T. Problem Read this addition word problem to children.

- **Ten children are on the bus. Seven of the children are girls. How many children are boys?** 3

Go Deeper

To extend their thinking, have children talk about how they might be able to solve this problem without acting it out or modeling it. For example, some children might say that they would count the numbers they say after 7 until they reach 10.

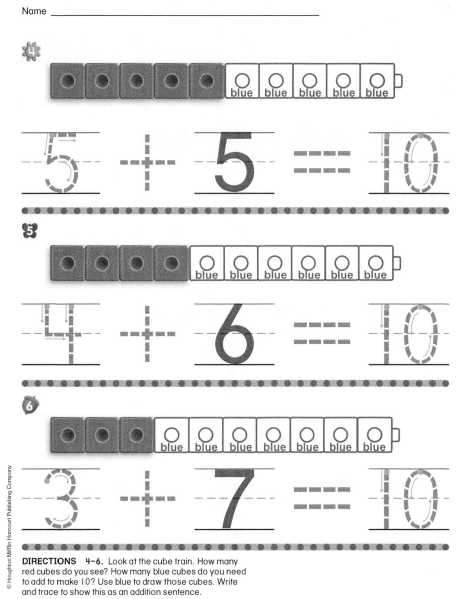

DIRECTIONS 4–6. Look at the cube train. How many red cubes do you see? How many blue cubes do you need to add to make 10? Use blue to draw those cubes. Write and trace to show this as an addition sentence.

Chapter 5 • Lesson 5   one hundred eighty-seven **187**

PROBLEM SOLVING REAL WORLD

① 2 + 8 = 10

Check children's work.

② 1 + 9 = 10

Check children's work.

DIRECTIONS 1. Troy has 2 ducks. How many more ducks does he need to get to have 10 ducks in all? Draw to solve the problem. Trace and write to show this as an addition sentence. 2. Draw to find the number that makes 10 when put together with the given number. Trace and write to show this as an addition sentence.

188 one hundred eighty-eight

 HOME ACTIVITY · Show your child a number from 1 to 9. Ask him or her to find the number that makes 10 when put together with that number. Then have him or her tell a story to go with the problem.

FOR MORE PRACTICE:
Standards Practice Book, pp. P89–P90

© Houghton Mifflin Harcourt Publishing Company

► **Problem Solving**

Have children listen to the problem for Exercise 1.

- **Troy has 2 ducks. How many more ducks does he need to get to have 10 ducks in all?**

- **How can you draw to show the information in the problem?** I can draw 2 ducks. Then I can draw more ducks until I draw all 10 ducks that Troy needs.

- **How can you use your drawing to help you find how many more ducks Troy needs?** I can count the ducks I drew after the 2 ducks that Troy already has.

Have children make their drawings and complete the addition sentence.

For Exercise 2, have children make a drawing and complete the addition sentence to find a number that makes 10 when put together with the given number.

Have children share and explain their drawings and addition sentences.

4 SUMMARIZE

Essential Question

How can you use a drawing to find the number that makes a ten from a given number? Possible answer: I can draw the number of objects I am given. Then I can draw more objects until I have 10 of them. I can count how many more I needed to draw and write that number in the addition sentence.

Differentiated Instruction — INDEPENDENT ACTIVITIES

Grab-and-Go!™

Differentiated Centers Kit

Activities
All Together Now!
Children complete the purple Activity Card 6 by using two-color counters in combinations that add up to 9.

Literature
Flowers for Flossie
Children read the book and count and add flowers of different colors.

Games
Spin to Add
Children use connecting cubes to model addition problems.

Digital Path

- Animated Math Models
- iT iTools
- MM HMH Mega Math
- Soar to Success Math
- eStudent Edition

Algebra • Write Addition Sentences

LESSON AT A GLANCE

Common Core Standard

Understand addition as putting together and adding to, and understand subtraction as taking apart and taking from.

CC.K.OA.5 Fluently add and subtract within 5.

Also CC.K.OA.1, CC.K.OA.2

Lesson Objective

Solve addition word problems within 5 and record the equation.

Essential Question

How can you solve addition word problems and complete the addition sentence?

Materials

MathBoard

Digital Path

- ☑ Animated Math Models
- iT *iTools:* Counters
- 🞯 eStudent Edition

iT *iTools:* Counters

COMMON CORE PROFESSIONAL DEVELOPMENT

About the Math

Teaching for Depth

In this lesson, children will work with an addition situation that provides a starting number and has them find the number to add to arrive at a given sum. For example, three children were at the table. Some more children came and now there are five children. How many more children came over?

Children need to understand what information is given and what information is unknown, missing, or needs to be found. When they are telling their addition word problems, they should look at the numbers provided in the addition sentence and use the first addend and the sum as the givens in their problems. Make sure children understand how to create their own addition with an addend as the unknown or missing number.

Professional Development Video Podcasts

Daily Routines 🟦 Math Board

Common Core

SPIRAL REVIEW

eTransparency
5.6

Problem of the Day

Number of the Day Find 4 on the calendar.

Show four fingers.

Have children tell you what they know about the number 4.

Vocabulary Builder

Materials Vocabulary cards for *plus* and *add* (see *eTeacher Resources*)

Plus

Show the card for *plus* and draw a *plus* symbol on the board. Discuss what the word and symbol mean.

- **Plus tells you that you will add.** Hold up the *add* card. **When you put two sets or two numbers together, you add them.**

Choose six children to model this addition word problem.

- **Two children were in a line. Four more children joined the line. How many children are in the line now?** 6

- **When you talk about the addition word problem you can say 2 plus 4 is 6. You can use the word *plus* to show that you are putting together groups of children or putting together sets of objects.**

Literature Big Book

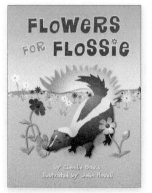

From the Grab-and-Go™ Differentiated Centers Kit

Children read the book and count and add flowers of different colors.

Flowers for Flossie

Differentiated Instruction Activities

ELL Language Support
Kinesthetic / Small Group

Strategy: Model Concepts

Materials connecting cubes

Children may understand addition word problems if they are modeled.

- Write 2 + _____ = 4 on the board.
- **Lee has two cubes. He finds some more cubes. Now he has four cubes. How many cubes did he find?**
- Have children start with two cubes. Have them add more until they have four.
- **How many more cubes did you add?** 2

Have a volunteer complete the addition sentence. Repeat with other examples.

See **ELL** Activity Guide for leveled activities.

Enrich
Kinesthetic / Visual / Individual / Partners

Materials crayons

Ask children to draw a picture to go with the following addition word problem.

- **Six cubes are on a table. More cubes are put on the table. Now there are nine cubes. How many more cubes were put on the table?**
- Have children circle the set they started with.
- Have children complete an addition sentence.

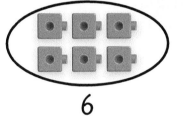

6   3

RtI Response to Intervention

Reteach Tier 1
Kinesthetic / Visual / Whole Class / Small Group

Materials two-color counters, crayons

Provide children with five counters and paper. Have them make a set of three red counters. Then have them draw three red counters on their paper and write the numeral 3 below them.

- Have children make another set with the remaining counters on the yellow side and draw them.
- **Circle the set you started with. How many counters are there in all?** 5 **How many more counters did you add?** 2
- Write an addition sentence for children to complete on the board and have them take turns writing the numbers to represent their sets, 2 + 3 = 5.

Repeat the activity with a different number of counters.

Tier 2
Visual / Kinesthetic / Visual / Small Group

Materials crayons

Place two crayons on the table. Have children draw a picture of two crayons on their paper. Then have them write the number 2 below the drawing.

- **Find how many to add to make 3.**
- Write 2 + _____ = 3 on the board.
- **How many crayons are there in all?** 3
- Start with two crayons. Have a volunteer add crayons to make 3.
- **How many crayons added to 2 make 3?** 1
- Have children complete the addition sentence. 2 + 1 = 3

2   1

1 ENGAGE

Materials connecting cubes

Access Prior Knowledge Introduce the lesson by showing and saying the following:

• **I have three cubes in my right hand. How can you show the cubes on a MathBoard?** I can draw a picture that shows a three-cube train.

• **I have three cubes in my left hand. How can you show the cubes on the MathBoard?** I can draw another picture that shows a three-cube train.

Have children draw each cube train. Draw one circle around the two cube trains. Ask a volunteer to count the cubes to find how many in all. 6

Repeat with other cube trains.

2 TEACH and TALK GO Online · Animated Math Models

▶ **Listen and Draw** MATHEMATICAL PRACTICES

Read aloud this addition word problem.

There are two fish. Some more fish swim over. Now there are three fish. How many fish swam over?

• **What information do you know?** There were two fish and now there are three fish.

• **What information do you have to find?** how many more fish swam over

• **How many fish were there to start?** 2

Instruct children to circle the two fish.

• **How many fish are being added to the set?** 1

• **How many are there now?** 3

Reread the original problem.

• **How many fish swam over?** 1

• **Trace the addition sentence.**

Have children read the addition sentence. 2 plus 1 is equal to 3

Discuss how the second number of the addition sentence was unknown or missing. Have children take turns explaining how they found the unknown or missing number.

MATHEMATICAL PRACTICES **Do you always have to add things that are alike? Explain.**

189 Chapter 5

COMMON CORE

CCK.OA.5 Fluently add and subtract within 5.

Name _____

Lesson 5.6

Algebra • Write Addition Sentences

Essential Question How can you solve addition word problems and complete the addition sentence?

COMMON CORE STANDARD CC.K.OA.5
Understand addition as putting together and adding to, and understand subtraction as taking apart and taking from.

Listen and Draw REAL WORLD

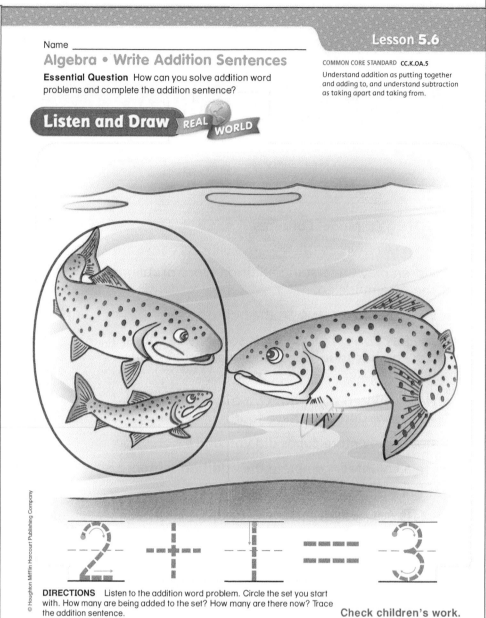

$$2 + 1 = 3$$

DIRECTIONS Listen to the addition word problem. Circle the set you start with. How many are being added to the set? How many are there now? Trace the addition sentence.

Check children's work.

Chapter 5 · Lesson 6

one hundred eighty-nine **189**

Standards Practice 5.6

Common Core SPIRAL REVIEW

Name _____

Lesson 5.6

Algebra • Write Addition Sentences

COMMON CORE STANDARD CC.K.OA.5
Understand addition as putting together and adding to, and understand subtraction as taking apart and taking from.

$$3 + 2 = 5$$

$$1 + 3 = 4$$

$$4 + 1 = 5$$

DIRECTIONS 1–3. Tell an addition word problem about the sets. Circle the set you start with. How many are being added to the set? How many are there now? Write and trace to complete the addition sentence.

Chapter 5

ninety-one **P91**

Lesson Check (CC.K.OA.5)

$$3 + \underline{\quad} = 5$$

| 1 | 2 | 3 | 4 |
| ○ | ● | ○ | ○ |

Spiral Review (CC.K.CC.5, CC.K.CC.5)

| 1 | 2 | 3 | 4 |
| ○ | ● | ○ | ○ |

DIRECTIONS 1. Which number completes the addition sentence about the sets of airplanes? Mark under your answer. (Lesson 5.6) 2. How many more counters would you place to model a way to make 8? Mark under your answer. (Lesson 3.5) 3. How many paintbrushes are there? Mark under your answer. (Lesson 1.4)

P92 ninety-two

Share and Show

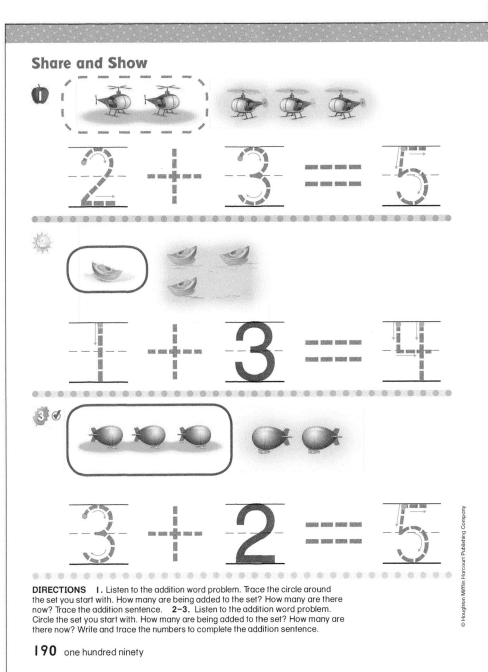

DIRECTIONS 1. Listen to the addition word problem. Trace the circle around the set you start with. How many are being added to the set? How many are there now? Trace the addition sentence. 2–3. Listen to the addition word problem. Circle the set you start with. How many are being added to the set? How many are there now? Write and trace the numbers to complete the addition sentence.

190 one hundred ninety

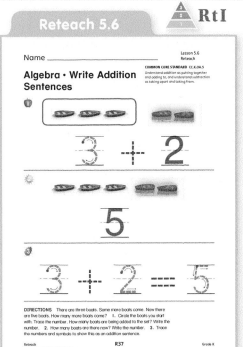

Reteach 5.6 ▲ **RtI**

Name _____ Lesson 5.6 Reteach

COMMON CORE STANDARD CC.K.OA.5
Understand addition as putting together and adding to, and understand subtraction as taking apart and taking from.

Algebra • Write Addition Sentences

DIRECTIONS There are three boats. Some more boats come. Now there are five boats. How many more boats come? 1. Circle the boats you start with. Trace the number. 2. How many boats are there now? Write the number. 3. Trace the numbers and symbols to show this as an addition sentence.

Reteach R37   Grade K
© Houghton Mifflin Harcourt Publishing Company

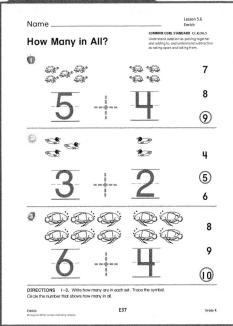

Enrich 5.6

Name _____ Lesson 5.6 Enrich

COMMON CORE STANDARD CC.K.OA.5
Understand addition as putting together and adding to, and understand subtraction as taking apart and taking from.

How Many in All?

DIRECTIONS 1–3. Write how many are in each set. Trace the symbol. Circle the number that shows how many in all.

Enrich E37   Grade K
© Houghton Mifflin Harcourt Publishing Company

---

3 PRACTICE

▶ Share and Show • Guided Practice

Have children look at Exercise 1.

There are two helicopters. Some more helicopters land. Now there are five helicopters. How many helicopters land?

- **What information do you know?** There were two helicopters and now there are five.
- **What information do you have to find?** how many more helicopters land
- **How many helicopters are there to start?** 2 **Trace the circle around them.**
- **How many helicopters are being added to the set?** 3 **Trace the number.**
- **How many are there now?** 5
- **Trace to complete the addition sentence.**

Have children complete Exercises 2 and 3 in the same way using these addition word problems:

- **One boat is on the shore. Some more boats come. Now there are four boats on the shore. How many more boats come?** 3
- **There are three blimps. Some more blimps land. Now there are five blimps. How many blimps land?**

Use Exercise 3 for Quick Check.

✔ Quick Check ▲ RtI

If a child misses Exercise 3

Then **Differentiate Instruction** with
- RtI Tier 1 Activity, p. 189B
- Reteach 5.6
- ✷ Soar to Success Math 10.04

⚠ COMMON ERRORS

Error Children may put the sum as the missing addend.

Example Children put 4 as the second addend in Exercise 2.

Springboard to Learning Hide the second set, and ask children to count the number in the first set and trace the number. Then cover the first set, and have children count the second set and write the number.

Lesson 5.6 190

► More Practice

Have children find Exercise 4. Ask a volunteer to tell an addition word problem. Explain that the second addend should be unknown or missing to match the addition sentence.

- **How many boats are in the set you started with?** 1 **Circle that set.**
- **How many boats are being added to the set?** 4 **Write the number.**
- **How many boats are there now?** 5
- **Trace to complete the addition sentence.**

For Exercises 5 through 6, have children take turns telling addition word problems about the pictures. Have children circle the first set. Have them count how many are in the second set and write the number. Then have them trace to complete the addition sentence.

H.O.T. Problem Ask children to draw a picture on their MathBoards to go with the following addition word problem.

- **I saw two boats on one side of the lake. Then I saw some more boats on the other side. I saw five boats on the lake.**
- **How many boats did I see on the other side of the lake?** 3

Go Deeper
MATHEMATICAL PRACTICES

Children have now taken it one step further by drawing the pictures for an addition word problem. Invite children to take turns telling an addition word problem about boats.

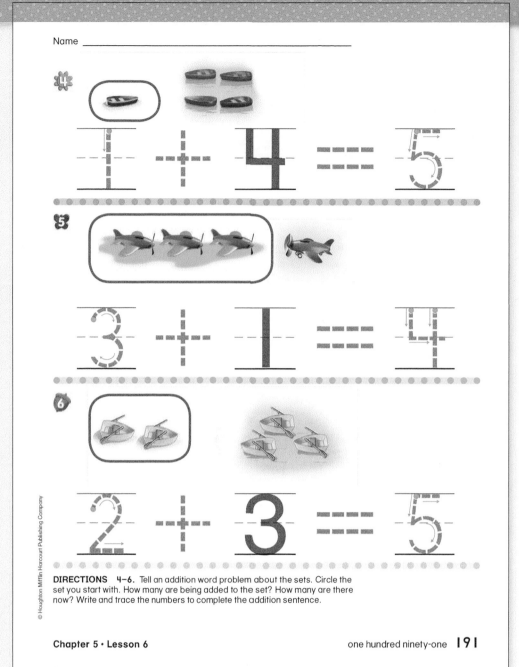

DIRECTIONS 4–6. Tell an addition word problem about the sets. Circle the set you start with. How many are being added to the set? How many are there now? Write and trace the numbers to complete the addition sentence.

Chapter 5 · Lesson 6

one hundred ninety-one 191

COMMON CORE

PROFESSIONAL DEVELOPMENT — Math Talk in Action

While working on the H.O.T. Problem, children discussed some questions and ideas.

Ava: I drew a circle to show the lake. Now I am using boxes for the boats. I drew two boats on one side and I need to draw five boats on the lake. I am not sure how many more boats to draw.

Olivia: I think that you can count to figure that out.

Jacob: You could draw one more and count how many that is and then draw another one and count that many until you get to 5.

Teacher: Did anyone figure this out a different way?

Tyrone: I did. I thought of what I could add to 2 to make 5.

Jane: I drew five boats outside the lake and then put them in the lake.

Teacher: Do you think you can use one of these ideas, Ava?

Ava: I am going to try Jacob's way.

Teacher: Who can tell an addition word problem about the boats?

Jane: There were two boats at the dock. Some more boats docked. Now there are 5. How many more boats docked?

Tyrone: I know the answer because she changed the problem but used the same numbers. The answer is three. Two plus three more makes 5.

Teacher: You are all doing a fine job. Now think of some more word problems with boats using different numbers.

PROBLEM SOLVING REAL WORLD

1

$2 + 2 = 4$

Check children's work.

$\underline{\quad} + \underline{\quad} = \underline{\quad}$

Check children's work.

DIRECTIONS 1. Bill catches two fish. Jake catches some fish. They catch four fish in all. How many fish does Jake catch? Draw to show the fish. Trace and write to complete the addition sentence. 2. Tell a different addition word problem about fish. Draw to show the fish. Tell about your drawing. Complete the addition sentence.

 HOME ACTIVITY • Have your child show three fingers. Have him or her show more fingers to make five fingers in all. Then have him or her tell how many more fingers he or she showed.

192 one hundred ninety-two

FOR MORE PRACTICE:
Standards Practice Book, pp. P91–P92

► **Problem Solving** MATHEMATICAL PRACTICES

Have children listen to the addition word problem.

• **Bill catches two fish. Jake catches some fish. They catch four fish in all. How many fish does Jake catch?**

Have children draw to show the fish. Then have them trace and write to complete the addition sentence.

For Exercise 2, have children tell a different addition word problem about fish and draw the fish. Then have them complete the addition sentence. Children might draw two sets, circle the first set, and write an addition sentence below.

 Encourage children to tell about their drawings to a partner. Then choose several children to discuss their drawings and sentences with the class.

4 SUMMARIZE MATHEMATICAL PRACTICES

Essential Question

How can you solve addition word problems and complete the addition sentence? I can see how many objects are being added to the first set to make the number of objects in all. I can fill in that missing number to complete the addition sentence.

Differentiated Instruction — INDEPENDENT ACTIVITIES

Grab-and-Go! Differentiated Centers Kit

Activities
Get It Together!
Children complete the blue Activity Card 6 by using various objects to make up and show different addition combinations.

Literature
Flowers for Flossie
Children read the book and count and add flowers of different colors.

Games
Spin to Add
Children use connecting cubes to model addition problems.

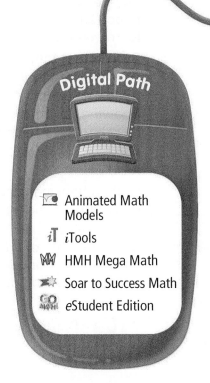
Digital Path

- Animated Math Models
- iTools
- HMH Mega Math
- Soar to Success Math
- eStudent Edition

Algebra • Write More Addition Sentences

LESSON AT A GLANCE

Common Core Standard

Understand addition as putting together and adding to, and understand subtraction as taking apart and taking from.

CC.K.OA.2 Solve addition and subtraction word problems, and add and subtract within 10, e.g., by using objects or drawings to represent the problem.

Also CC.K.OA.1

Lesson Objective

Solve addition word problems within 10 and record the equation

Essential Question

How can you solve addition word problems and complete the addition sentence?

Materials

MathBoard

Digital Path

☑ Animated Math Models
𝖬𝖬 HMH Mega Math
𝑖𝖳 iTools: Counters
eStudent Edition

COMMON CORE PROFESSIONAL DEVELOPMENT

About the Math

Why Teach This

Children may ask why they need to learn this. It is important for children to understand why they need to learn about addition.

Explain that they use addition often and may not even realize it. Give children examples of times when they have used addition in everyday situations such as:

Knowing how many plates to set on the table when they have a friend come over.

Knowing how many toy cars they have if four are red and five are blue.

Finding how many buttons they started with when two more buttons makes 7 in all.

During this chapter, children have worked with many different types of addition situations. In this lesson, children will work with the situation of adding to an unknown starting number.

Professional Development Video Podcasts

Daily Routines

Math Board

Common Core

SPIRAL REVIEW

Problem of the Day

eTransparency
5.7

Number of the Day Join your hands together. How many fingers do you have in all?
10

You have five fingers on one hand and five on the other hand. You could say that 5 and 5 is equal to 10.

Lead children in counting to 10. Have them show all ten fingers. Have children repeat the sentence that describes addition.

Fluency Builder

Materials Number and Symbol Tiles (front)
(see *eTeacher Resources*)

Number Sequence

Have ten children each hold a number tile from 1 to 10 in order. Lead children in saying the numbers in order.

Differentiated Instruction Activities

ELL Language Support
 Kinesthetic
Small Group

Strategy: Identify Relationships

Materials connecting cubes

Children can learn the concept of missing addends by relating common objects to addition word problems.

- **I have a blue cube train. I add five red cubes to the blue cubes.** Display a five-cube red train.
- **Now my train has eight cubes in all.** Write _____ + 5 = 8 on the board.
- **How many blue cubes did I start with?** 3 Attach a three-cube blue train to the red train.
- Write **3 + 5 = 8.** Have children say this addition sentence aloud.

See **ELL** Activity Guide for leveled activities.

Enrich
 Kinesthetic
Partners

Materials Numeral Cards (0–7), (8–15) (see *eTeacher Resources*)

Each set of partners should have two sets of numeral cards, 1 to 5 and 6 to 10.

Have partners play a game of, *"What Number Did You Start With?"*

- Have one partner select a card from the 1 to 5 set of cards and write the number as the second addend in the addition sentence.
- Have the other partner select a card from the 6 to 10 set and write the number as the sum in the addition sentence.
- Then have partners work together to complete the addition sentence that tells what number should be the first addend in the addition sentence.

5   9

RtI Response to Intervention

Reteach Tier 1
 Kinesthetic / Visual
Whole Class / Small Group

Materials two-color counters, cups, paper, crayons

Provide each child with two counters and a cup filled with five counters.

- Have children draw two counters on paper and then place the two counters in their cup.
- Ask children to gently spill the counters from the cup onto their desk.
- Have children count aloud how many counters in all. 7
- **How many counters were in the cup before?** 5
- Ask children to draw a total of seven counters on their paper.
- Have children complete an addition sentence. 5 + 2 = 7

Repeat the activity with different numbers of counters.

Tier 2
 Visual / Kinesthetic
Small Group

Materials cup, crayons

Place two crayons hidden under a cup on the table. Next to the cup, place five crayons on the table.

- Have children draw five crayons on their paper and write 5 below their drawing.
- **Now I have seven crayons in all.** Have children draw more crayons on their paper to make 7.
- Write _____ + 5 = 7.
- **How many crayons are under my cup?** 2 Lift the cup to show children two crayons.
- **How many crayons did I start with?** 2 Have children complete the addition sentence. 2 + 5 = 7

1 ENGAGE

Access Prior Knowledge Have a class discussion about birds.

- **Where have you seen birds?** Possible answers: outside, pet store, friend's house, park

- **What is alike about all birds? What is different?** Possible answers: They all have two feet, feathers, and a beak. They are different sizes and colors.

- **What do you know about birds?** Possible answers: they have feathers, lay eggs, sing, some can talk

2 TEACH and TALK **GO** Online Animated Math Models

▶ **Listen and Draw** (MATHEMATICAL PRACTICES)

Read aloud this addition word problem.

Some birds were sitting on a branch. one more bird flew there. Now there are five birds on the branch. How many birds were on the branch before?

- **What information do you know?** One bird flew there and now there are five birds on the branch.

- **What information do you have to find?** how many birds were on the branch before

- **How many more birds flew over?** 1

Instruct children to circle the bird that is being added.

- **How many birds were there to start?** 4

Have children count the birds that are not in the circle to find how many there were to start.

- **How many birds are there now?** 5

Discuss how the first number of the addition sentence was the unknown or missing number in the addition word problem.

- **Trace the addition sentence.**

Have children read the addition sentence. Encourage them to use the correct wording when reading the addition sentence. 4 plus 1 is equal to 5

COMMON CORE

CC.K.OA.2 Solve addition and subtraction word problems, and add and subtract within 10, e.g., by using objects or drawings to represent the problem.

Name _____

Lesson 5.7

Algebra • Write More Addition Sentences

COMMON CORE STANDARD CC.K.OA.2
Understand addition as putting together and adding to, and understand subtraction as taking apart and taking from.

Essential Question How can you solve addition word problems and complete the addition sentence?

Listen and Draw

DIRECTIONS Listen to the addition word problem about the birds. Circle the bird joining the other birds. How many birds did you start with? Trace the circle around that number. Trace the addition sentence.

Check children's work.

Chapter 5 • Lesson 7

one hundred ninety-three **193**

Standards Practice 5.7

Common Core   SPIRAL REVIEW

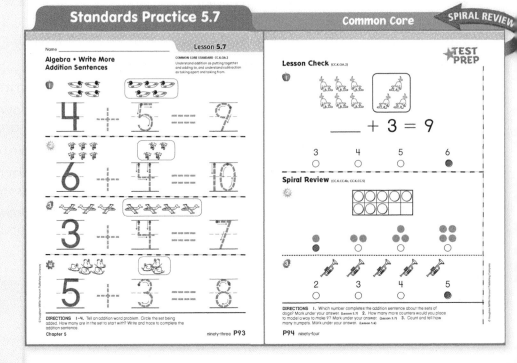

Name _____

Lesson 5.7

Algebra • Write More Addition Sentences

COMMON CORE STANDARD CC.K.OA.2
Understand addition as putting together and adding to, and understand subtraction as taking apart and taking from.

DIRECTIONS 1–4. Tell an addition word problem. Circle the set being added. How many are in the set to start with? Write and trace to complete the addition sentence.

Chapter 5

ninety-three P93

Lesson Check (CC.K.OA.2)

____ + 3 = 9

3   4   5   6
○   ○   ○   ○

Spiral Review (CC.K.CC.4b, CC.K.CC.5)

2   3   4   5
○   ○   ○   ○

DIRECTIONS 1. Which number completes the addition sentence about the sets of dogs? Mark under your answer. (Lesson 5.7) 2. How many more counters would you place to model a way to make 9? Mark under your answer. (Lesson 3.7) 3. Count and tell how many trumpets. Mark under your answer. (Lesson 1.6)

P94 ninety-four

Share and Show

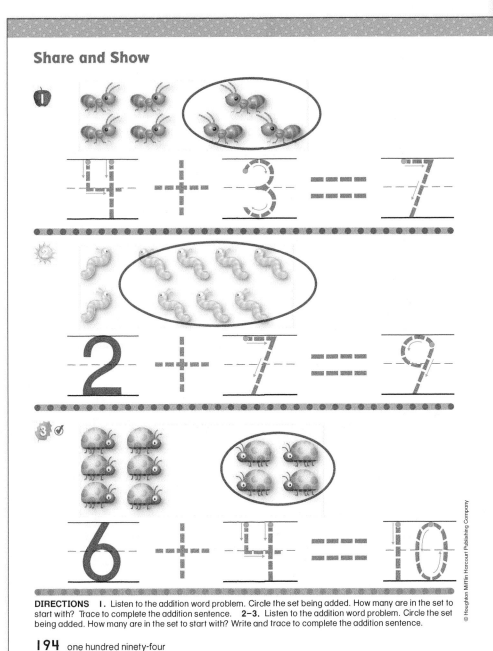

1. $4 + 3 = 7$

2. $2 + 7 = 9$

3. $6 + 4 = 10$

DIRECTIONS 1. Listen to the addition word problem. Circle the set being added. How many are in the set to start with? Trace to complete the addition sentence. **2–3.** Listen to the addition word problem. Circle the set being added. How many are in the set to start with? Write and trace to complete the addition sentence.

194 one hundred ninety-four

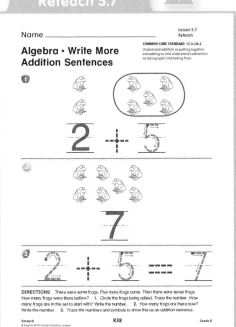
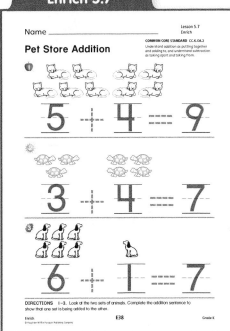
3 PRACTICE

▶ **Share and Show •** Guided Practice

Work through Exercise 1 with children.

There were some ants. Three more ants come to visit. Then there were seven ants. How many ants were there before?

• **How many ants come to visit?** 3

• **Circle the ants that are being added.**

• **How many ants were there before?** 4

Have children count the ants that are not in the circle to find how many there were before.

Have children count all the ants.

• **How many ants are there now?** 7

• **Trace to complete the addition sentence.**

Have children read the addition sentence that shows what is happening in the picture. Encourage children to use the correct wording. 4 plus 3 is equal to 7

Have children complete Exercises 2 and 3 in the same way using these addition word problems:

There were some worms. Seven more worms wiggled over. Then there were nine worms. How many worms were there to start? 2

Some bugs were playing. Four more bugs came to play. Then there were ten bugs. How many bugs were there before? 6

Use Exercise 3 for Quick Check.

✔ **Quick Check**  RtI

If ▶ a child misses Exercise 3

Then ▶ **Differentiate Instruction** with
• RtI Tier 1 Activity, p. 193B
• Reteach 5.7
☆ Soar to Success Math 10.09

! COMMON ERRORS

Error Children may put the sum in the place of the missing addend.

Example Children look at Exercise 2 and count nine worms instead of the two worms in the first set.

Springboard to Learning Help children understand the sets by covering one set while counting and writing the number for that set.

► More Practice

For Exercises 4 through 6, ask children to tell an addition word problem. Remind them that the first number should be the unknown number. Have children circle the set being added. Then have them complete the addition sentence. Remind children to trace the symbols. Read the completed addition sentence together.

H.O.T. Problem Make a drawing of the bugs from Exercise 5 on the board and tell an addition word problem. This time, show three bugs first and then six bugs. Write the addition sentence _____ + 6 = 9.

- **What is the same about the picture in Exercise 5 and the picture on the board?**
  Possible answer: They both show bugs. **What is different?** Possible answer: The second set has 6 instead of 3.

- **How many bugs do you see in all?** 9

- **What addition sentence could you write to match this picture?** 3 + 6 = 9

Go Deeper

MATHEMATICAL PRACTICES

Children will compare related addition sentences to see the order property. Write the addition sentence 6 + 3 = 9 from Exercise 5 on the board. Under it, write 3 + 6 = 9.

Ask children to suggest reasons why the answer to both addition sentences is 9. Elicit that there is a set of 6 and a set of 3 in both addition sentences, but that the sets are in a different order.

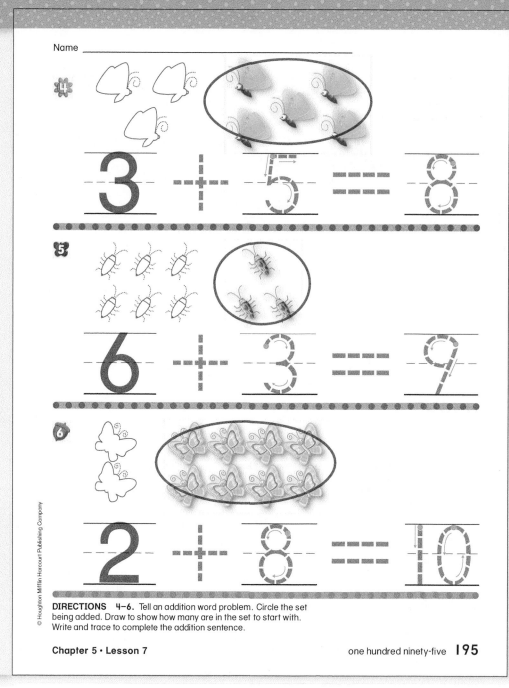

Name _____

$3 + 5 = 8$

$6 + 3 = 9$

$2 + 8 = 10$

DIRECTIONS 4–6. Tell an addition word problem. Circle the set being added. Draw to show how many are in the set to start with. Write and trace to complete the addition sentence.

Chapter 5 · Lesson 7

one hundred ninety-five **195**

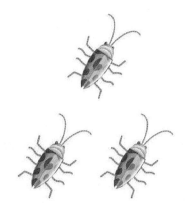 

$$3 + 6 = 9$$

PROBLEM SOLVING

$$7 = 5 + 2$$

Check children's work.

 DIRECTIONS I. Read the addition sentence. Draw to show what you know about the addition sentence. Tell a friend about your drawing.

 HOME ACTIVITY · Tell your child an addition word problem such as: There are some socks in the drawer. I added four more socks. Now there are ten socks in the drawer. How many socks were in the drawer to start with?

196 one hundred ninety-six

FOR MORE PRACTICE:
Standards Practice Book, pp. P93–P94

© Houghton Mifflin Harcourt Publishing Company

▶ **Problem Solving**

Call attention to the addition sentence on the top of the page. Explain to children that this is another way to show an addition sentence or equation. It is called an equation because the quantity on both sides of the *is equal to* symbol is the same quantity.

Explain that the positioning of the total does not matter as long as both sides of the *is equal to* symbol have the same quantity.

- **What numbers are being added?** 5 and 2

 Have children suggest different items that they might draw to illustrate the addition sentence. After children draw, ask volunteers to share their drawings and tell about them. Children should be able to explain that 7 is equal to a set of 5 and a set of 2.

4 SUMMARIZE   MATHEMATICAL PRACTICES

Essential Question

How can you solve addition word problems and complete the addition sentence? I can find how many objects there are at the start. Then I can fill in that unknown number to complete the addition sentence.

Differentiated Instruction   INDEPENDENT ACTIVITIES

Grab-and-Go!
Differentiated Centers Kit

Activities
Together Again!

Children complete the blue Activity Card 18 by modeling addition with two groups of shapes and writing the corresponding addition sentence.

Literature
Flowers for Flossie

Children read the book and count and add flowers of different colors.

Games
Spin to Add

 Games

Children use connecting cubes to model addition problems.

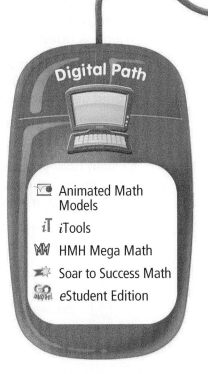

Digital Path

- Animated Math Models
- *i*T *i*Tools
- HMH Mega Math
- Soar to Success Math
- eStudent Edition

Hands On: Algebra • Number Pairs to 5

LESSON AT A GLANCE

Common Core Standard

Understand addition as putting together and adding to, and understand subtraction as taking apart and taking from.

CC.K.OA.3 Decompose numbers less than or equal to 10 into pairs in more than one way, e.g., by using objects or drawings, and record each decomposition by a drawing or equation (e.g., $5 = 2 + 3$ and $5 = 4 + 1$).

Also CC.K.OA.1, CC.K.OA.2

Lesson Objective

Decompose numbers within 5 into pairs in more than one way and record each decomposition with an equation.

Essential Question

How can you model and write addition sentences for number pairs for sums to 5?

Materials

MathBoard, connecting cubes

Digital Path

- ☑ **Animated Math Models**
- 🄶 **eStudent Edition**
- i⃗ℐ **iTools: Counters**

COMMON CORE
PROFESSIONAL DEVELOPMENT

About the Math

Teaching for Depth

As children work with addition, guide them to get into the routine of checking themselves. Reread the problems. Then ask questions similar to these:

Did you use the numbers that were used in the addition word problem? What kind of answer did you think you would get? Does your answer make sense?

Help children explain how they solved the problems with prompts such as these:

Explain how you found your answer.
Why did you choose that way to solve?
Is there another way you could have used to solve?

As you go through these questions, help children realize when they have made errors and guide them to correct those errors.

Professional Development Video Podcasts

Daily Routines

 Math Board

Common Core

Problem of the Day

 eTransparency 5.8

Number of the Day Find the number 10 on the calendar.
Show 10 with your fingers.
What can you tell about the number 10?
Possible answers: 5 and 5 makes 10; 10 has a 1 and a 0.
Discuss what ten counters would look like in a ten frame.

Fluency Builder

Materials Addition Fact Cards (within 5) (see *eTeacher Resources*)

Add Within 5

Have two children come to the front of the room. Have two more children join them.

How many children came first? 2
How many children came next? 2

Have children complete an addition sentence. $2 + 2 = 4$

Have one more child join them.

How many children were there first? 4
How many more children came? 1

Have children complete an addition sentence. $4 + 1 = 5$

Show addition fact cards for $2 + 2$ and $4 + 1$

Ask children to state the sums for each fact.

Differentiated Instruction Activities

ELL Language Support
 Kinesthetic / Visual
Small Group

Strategy: Describe

Materials connecting cubes (two different colors)

Write **5** on the board. Have children build a five-cube train using any combination of connecting cubes.

- Have a child describe how he or she built the cube train. Model proper language to help the child. **5 is equal to 1 plus 4**.

- Draw connecting cubes on the board to match what the child describes.

- Take turns having children describe their addition sentences and record them on the board.

See **ELL** Activity Guide for leveled activities.

Enrich
 Kinesthetic / Logical
Individuals / Partners

Materials Numeral Cards (0–7) (see *eTeacher Resources*), two-color counters

One child turns over a card from a stack of numeral cards from 1 to 5.

- Using two-color counters, have the other child create an addition sentence to describe this number and write it.

- Children take turns writing possible addition sentences using different number pairs until they have all the possible pairs.

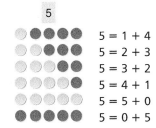

5	
⬤●●●●	5 = 1 + 4
⬤⬤●●●	5 = 2 + 3
⬤⬤⬤●●	5 = 3 + 2
⬤⬤⬤⬤●	5 = 4 + 1
⬤⬤⬤⬤⬤	5 = 5 + 0
●●●●●	5 = 0 + 5

RtI Response to Intervention

Reteach Tier 1
 Kinesthetic / Visual
Whole Class / Small Group

Write **3** on the board. Invite two children to the front of the room.

- **How many more do you need to make 3?** 1

- Invite another child to join the other children up front.

- Write the addition sentence on the board: **3 = 2 +1**

- Have children move themselves into sets for another pair of numbers that make 3.

- Have children write the matching addition sentence.

- Repeat with a different number of children of 5 or less.

Tier 2
 Visual / Kinesthetic
Small Group

Materials paper cups, two-color counters

Give each group a cup with five counters, paper, and crayons.

- One child spills the counters on a table. Each child writes an addition sentence that shows 5, which is the sum of the red and yellow counters.

- Have children compare their addition sentences to see if they are the same.

- Return the counters to the cup and repeat the activity. Lead children to discover that some children may write 5 = 1 + 4 and others may write 5 = 4 + 1, but the sum is the same. Then compare with other groups that may have 5 = 2 + 3.

$$5 = 1+4$$
$$5 = 4+1$$

1 ENGAGE iTools Online

Materials *i*Tools • Counters

Access Prior Knowledge Show three red counters and four yellow counters as a blank addition sentence.

- **What addition sentence do the counters show?** 3 + 4 = 7

Change one yellow counter to red so there are four red counters and three yellow counters.

- **Now what addition sentence do the counters show?** 4 + 3 = 7

Discuss how the two number sentences are the same or different. Repeat with other pairs of numbers.

2 TEACH and TALK GO Online Animated Math Models

▶ **Listen and Draw** MATHEMATICAL PRACTICES

Materials connecting cubes

Tiffany uses red and blue cubes to make a three-cube train. How many red cubes and how many blue cubes can she use?

- **What information is given in the problem?** Tiffany makes a cube train using three cubes. She uses red and blue cubes.

- **What information do you need to find?** The number of blue and the number of red cubes she can use to make the cube train.

- **Look at the addition sentence.**

- **Place two colors of cubes on the cube train to show a number pair that makes 3. Trace the addition sentence to show the number pair.**

- **Look at the addition sentence.**

- **Remove the cubes. Then place two colors of cubes on the cube train to show another number pair that makes 3. Trace that addition sentence.**

- **Read the addition sentences.** 3 is equal to 1 plus 2, and 3 is equal to 2 plus 1

Review with children that the total in the problem can be written on either side of the *is equal to* symbol. Both ways, for example, 3 = 1 + 2 and 1 + 2 = 3, are true addition sentences.

CC.K.OA.3 Decompose numbers less than or equal to 10 into pairs in more than one way. e.g., by using objects or drawings, and record each decomposition by a drawing or equation (e.g., 5 = 2 + 3 and 5 = 4 + 1).

COMMON CORE

Name _____

HANDS ON
Lesson 5.8

Algebra • Number Pairs to 5

Essential Question How can you model and write addition sentences for number pairs for sums to 5?

COMMON CORE STANDARD CC.K.OA.3
Understand addition as putting together and adding to, and understand subtraction as taking apart and taking from.

Listen and Draw

$3 = 1 + 2$

$3 = 2 + 1$

DIRECTIONS Place two colors of cubes on the cube train to show the number pairs that make 3. Trace the addition sentences to show some of the number pairs.

Check children's work.

Chapter 5 • Lesson 8

one hundred ninety-seven **197**

Standards Practice 5.8

Common Core SPIRAL REVIEW

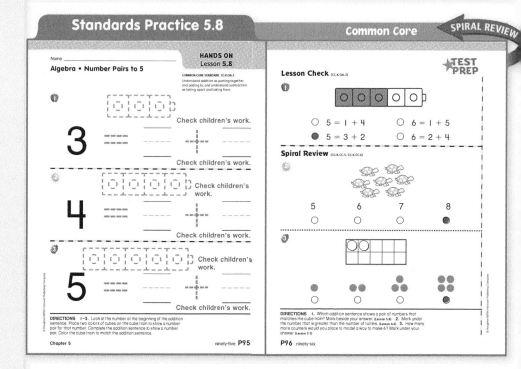

Share and Show

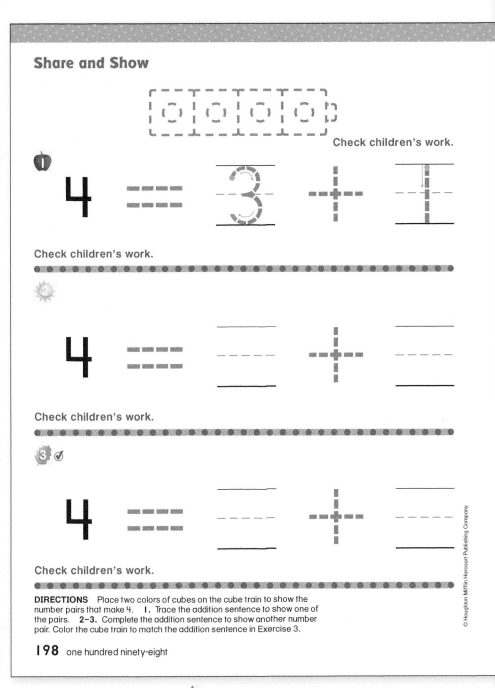

Check children's work.

1 4 === 3 + 1

Check children's work.

2 4 === ___ + ___

Check children's work.

3 4 === ___ + ___

Check children's work.

DIRECTIONS Place two colors of cubes on the cube train to show the number pairs that make 4. **1.** Trace the addition sentence to show one of the pairs. **2–3.** Complete the addition sentence to show another number pair. Color the cube train to match the addition sentence in Exercise 3.

198 one hundred ninety-eight

© Houghton Mifflin Harcourt Publishing Company

 PRACTICE Math Board

▶ **Share and Show** • Guided Practice

Have children locate Exercise 1.

- Place two colors of cubes on the cube train to show the number pairs that make 4.
- **How many red cubes will you use?** 3
- **How many blue cubes will you use?** 1
- **Trace the addition sentence.**

Children may also use 3 blue cubes and 1 red cube to show 4 = 3 + 1.

For Exercises 2 and 3, discuss possible number pairs that make 4 that are different than Exercise 1. Have children complete the addition sentences. Then have them color the cube train to match the addition sentence in Exercise 3.

Use Exercise 3 for Quick Check.

✔ Quick Check ▲RtI

If a child misses Exercise 3

Then Differentiate Instruction with
- RtI Tier 1 Activity, p. 197B
- Reteach 5.8
- ★ Soar to Success Math 10.09

⚠ COMMON ERRORS

Error Children may not understand that different number pairs can be used for the same sum.

Example In Exercise 2, children repeat 4 = 3 + 1 from Exercise 1.

Springboard to Learning Model how to trade one color cube for another color cube to make a new pair. Also model how to switch the order of the addends to make another pair.

▶ More Practice

Guide children to use two colors of cubes on the cube train to show number pairs that make 5.

For Exercises 4 through 7, after children use the cubes to find different number pairs, they can complete each addition sentence.

After they complete Exercise 7, have children color the cube train to match the addition sentence.

H.O.T. Problem How can you use the same numbers from a number pair to find a second number pair for the same total?

Go Deeper

Children must use what they know about number pairs to solve the H.O.T. Problem.

• **Does the order of numbers change the quantity?** Possible answer: I can change the order of which number I add first, or which number I add last. The order of numbers does not change the quantity because as long as the numbers are the same, the total is the same.

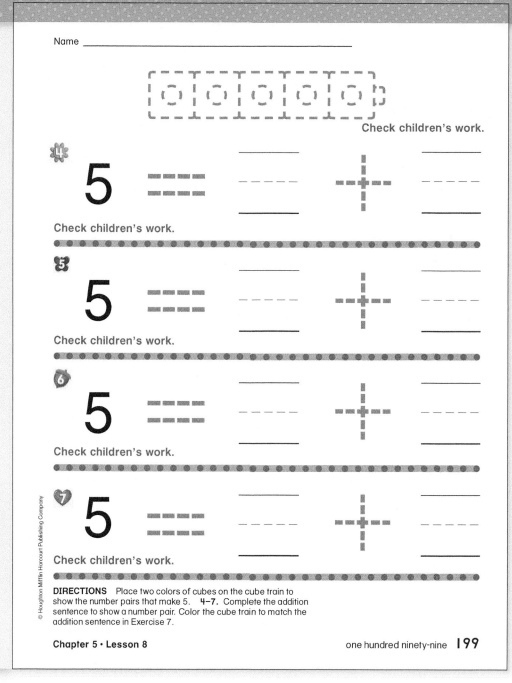

Name _____

Check children's work.

4 5 = ___ ___ + ___ ___

Check children's work.

5 5 = ___ ___ + ___ ___

Check children's work.

6 5 = ___ ___ + ___ ___

Check children's work.

7 5 = ___ ___ + ___ ___

Check children's work.

© Houghton Mifflin Harcourt Publishing Company

DIRECTIONS Place two colors of cubes on the cube train to show the number pairs that make 5. **4–7.** Complete the addition sentence to show a number pair. Color the cube train to match the addition sentence in Exercise 7.

Chapter 5 • Lesson 8   one hundred ninety-nine **199**

Cross-Curricular

SCIENCE

Materials gummed stars, folded paper

Talk about the fact that stars may look small in the sky, but stars are very large when seen up close.

• Have children paste three stars on one side of a page.
• Then have them paste one star on the other side.
• Have children count the stars on the paper and tell how many in all.
• Invite children to repeat the activity, using another folded paper and sums to 5.

SOCIAL STUDIES

Materials toy trucks and trains

Talk about how real trucks and trains travel all over the country, bringing people the food they need. Explain how food is something people need to survive. It is different than things people may want, such as toys.

• Have children draw two trains and two trucks.
• Have children count the number of vehicles in all and write the number.
• Then invite children to repeat the activity with two sets with sums to 5, show their drawings, and tell how many in all.

PROBLEM SOLVING REAL WORLD

$5 = \underline{} + \underline{}$

Child colors 5 of the cubes red. 5, 0

Check children's work.

DIRECTIONS 1. Peyton and Ashley have five red apples. Peyton is holding five of the apples. How many is Ashley holding? Color the cube train to show the number pair. Complete the addition sentence. **2.** Draw to show what you know about a number pair to 5.

HOME ACTIVITY · Have your child tell you the number pairs for a set of objects up to five. Have him or her tell an addition sentence for one of the number pairs.

200 two hundred

© Houghton Mifflin Harcourt Publishing Company

FOR MORE PRACTICE:
Standards Practice Book, pp. P95–P96

▶ **Problem Solving** MATHEMATICAL PRACTICES

Provide children with red crayons. Read the addition word problem aloud in Exercise 1. Help children understand that there are five apples in all.

- **How many apples is Peyton holding?** 5
- **If Peyton is holding five apples and there are five apples in all, how many apples is Ashley holding?** none
- **What number means none?** 0
- **What happens when you add 0 to a number?** The number does not change.
- **Color the cube train to show the number pair.** Children color five of the cubes one color [red]. **Complete the addition sentence.**

For Exercise 2, have children draw to show what they know about a number pair to 5.

Have children tell a partner about their drawings and their addition sentence.

4 SUMMARIZE MATHEMATICAL PRACTICES

Essential Question

How can you model and write addition sentences for number pairs for sums to 5? I can make two sets of cubes in different colors until I have the number in all. Then I can use the numbers to write the addition sentence.

Differentiated Instruction INDEPENDENT ACTIVITIES

Grab-and-Go!
Differentiated Centers Kit

Activities
Get It Together!

Children complete the blue Activity Card 6 by using various objects to make and show different addition combinations.

Literature
Flowers for Flossie

Children read the book and count and add flowers of different colors.

Games
Spin to Add

Children use connecting cubes to model addition problems.

Digital Path

- Animated Math Models
- iTools
- HMH Mega Math
- Soar to Success Math
- eStudent Edition

Hands On: Algebra • Number Pairs for 6 and 7

LESSON AT A GLANCE

Common Core Standard

Understand addition as putting together and adding to, and understand subtraction as taking apart and taking from.

CC.K.OA.3 Decompose numbers less than or equal to 10 into pairs in more than one way, e.g., by using objects or drawings, and record each decomposition by a drawing or equation (e.g., $5 = 2 + 3$ and $5 = 4 + 1$).

Also CC.K.OA.1, CC.K.OA.2

Lesson Objective

Decompose 6 and 7 into pairs in more than one way and record each decomposition with an equation.

Essential Question

How can you model and write addition sentences for number pairs for each sum of 6 and 7?

Materials

Math Board, connecting cubes

Digital Path

- Animated Math Models
- iTools: Counters
- eStudent Edition

Daily Routines

Common Core

SPIRAL REVIEW

Math Board

eTransparency **5.9**

Problem of the Day

Word of the Day What number is one greater than 8?

What number is one greater than 4?

What number is one greater than 9?

9; 5; 10

Review the meaning of *greater than* and give more problems with other numbers.

COMMON CORE MATHEMATICAL PRACTICES

Model Decomposing Numbers

Children are working with number pairs in this chapter. In this lesson and the lessons that follow, children are given a sum and can decompose that number into number pairs that make that number. By using two colors of connecting cubes, they are able to see what number pairs can come from a given number.

As children work to find pairs of addends to show the given number, they should come to realize that there are many number pairs that can make a given number. Discuss how to find all the pairs in the most efficient way. Help children discover how to use a pattern to help them find all the ways. Have them start with all of one color and decrease that color by 1 each time as they increase the second color by 1 each time.

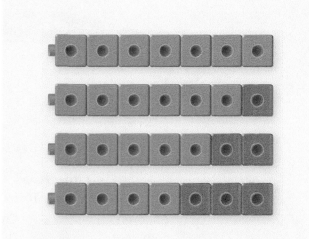

Differentiated Instruction Activities

ELL Language Support Kinesthetic Individual

Strategy: Model Concepts

Materials red and blue crayons

Children may understand concepts if they are illustrated.

- Draw six cubes in a row. Color four cubes red and write **4** under the cubes. Color two cubes blue and write **2** under the cubes. Write **6 = 4 + 2** under the cubes to show the addition sentence.

- Draw a set of seven cubes. Repeat the activity. Have children color five cubes red and two cubes blue. Write the number pair under the cubes. Write **7 = 5 + 2** to show the addition sentence.

See **ELL** Activity Guide for leveled activities.

Enrich Kinesthetic Partners

Materials seven red and seven blue connecting cubes

Children will use a pattern to find all the number pairs for 6 and 7.

- Have partners start with six red cubes and write the matching addition sentence, 6 = 6 + 0.

- Have them take away one red and add one blue cube to make a new number pair. Have them continue in the same way for each pair and write the addition sentence each time.

- Repeat for a sum of 7.

▲ RtI Response to Intervention

Reteach Tier 1 Kinesthetic / Visual Whole Class / Small Group

Materials connecting cubes

Model how to build these number pairs that make 6 using red and blue cubes: 6 + 0, 5 + 1, and 4 + 2.

- Explain that children can find other number pairs that make 6 by turning the cube trains so they face the opposite direction.

- Guide children to record the number sentences. Note that 3 + 3 is also a number pair that has a sum of 6, but does not make a new pair when turned.

- Repeat the activity for number pairs that make 7.

 6 = 5 + 1

 6 = 1 + 5

Tier 2 Visual / Kinesthetic Small Group

Materials connecting cubes

Read this problem to children. **Josh has seven cubes. Some are red and some are blue. How many cubes could he have of each color?**

- Show four red and three blue cubes in a row. **What number pair makes 7?** 4 and 3

- **What addition sentence can you write for this model?** Write **7 = 4 + 3** on the board.

- Ask children what they think will happen if the order of the number pairs are changed. Change the red cubes so they come after the blue cubes. **What addition sentence can you write for this model?** Write **7 = 3 + 4** on the board.

Discuss with children that Josh could have four red and three blue cubes or three red and four blue cubes, or any other combination that makes 7.

1 ENGAGE

Materials tape or yarn

Access Prior Knowledge Make two circles on the floor, each large enough for five children to stand in. Have three children stand in the first circle and have two children stand in the second circle. Call on other children to tell how many children are in each circle. 3 and 2

- **What addition sentence describes the total number of children in the circles?** 5 = 3 + 2 or 3 + 2 = 5

2 TEACH and TALK Animated Math Models

▶ **Listen and Draw**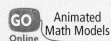

Materials connecting cubes

Read this addition word problem to the class.

Leslie made a six-cube train with red and blue cubes. How many of each color could she have used?

Read the first addition sentence with children. Point out the placement of the sum at the beginning of the addition sentence. Have them use cubes to model the six-cube train that matches the addition sentence and then color the cube train.

- **How many cubes are red?** 5 or 1 **How many are blue?** 1 or 5

Have children trace the addition sentence including the *is equal to* and the *plus* symbols.

- **How many cubes of each color could Leslie have used?** five red and one blue or five blue and one red

Point out the second cube train.

- **Andrew made a seven-cube train with red and blue cubes. How many of each color could he have used?**

Read the second addition sentence with children and have them model and then color the cube train.

- **How many cubes of each color could Andrew have used?** six red and one blue or six blue and one red

Have children trace the addition sentence.

Discuss with children that in this lesson they will learn many other ways to show 6 and 7.

CC.K.OA.3 Decompose numbers less than or equal to 10 into pairs in more than one way, e.g., by using objects or drawings, and record each decomposition by a drawing or equation (e.g., 5 = 2 + 3 and 5 = 4 + 1).

Name _____

Algebra • Number Pairs for 6 and 7

HANDS ON Lesson 5.9

Essential Question How can you model and write addition sentences for number pairs for each sum of 6 and 7?

COMMON CORE STANDARD CC.K.OA.3
Understand addition as putting together and adding to, and understand subtraction as taking apart and taking from.

Listen and Draw

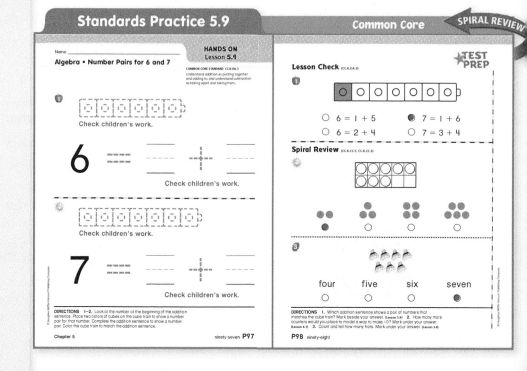

6 = 5 + 1

7 = 6 + 1

DIRECTIONS Place two colors of cubes on the cube trains to match the addition sentences. Color the cube trains. Trace the addition sentences.

Chapter 5 • Lesson 9

Check children's work.

two hundred one **201**

Standards Practice 5.9 **Common Core** SPIRAL REVIEW

Name _____

HANDS ON Lesson 5.9

Algebra • Number Pairs for 6 and 7

COMMON CORE STANDARD CC.K.OA.3
Understand addition as putting together and adding to, and understand subtraction as taking apart and taking from.

① Check children's work.

6 = ___ + ___

Check children's work.

② Check children's work.

7 = ___ + ___

Check children's work.

DIRECTIONS 1–2. Look at the number at the beginning of the addition sentence. Place two colors of cubes on the cube train to show a number pair for that number. Complete the addition sentence to show a number pair. Color the cube train to match the addition sentence.

Chapter 5

ninety-seven **P97**

Lesson Check (CC.K.OA.3)

①
○ 6 = 1 + 5   ● 7 = 1 + 6
○ 6 = 2 + 4   ○ 7 = 3 + 4

Spiral Review (CC.K.CC.5, CC.K.CC.3)

②
○   ○   ○   ●

③
four   five   six   seven
○   ○   ○   ●

DIRECTIONS 1. Which addition sentence shows a pair of numbers that matches the cube train? Mark beside your answer. (Lesson 5.9) 2. How many more counters would you place to model a way to make 10? Mark under your answer. (Lesson 4.1) 3. Count and tell how many hats. Mark under your answer. (Lesson 3.4)

P98 ninety-eight

Share and Show

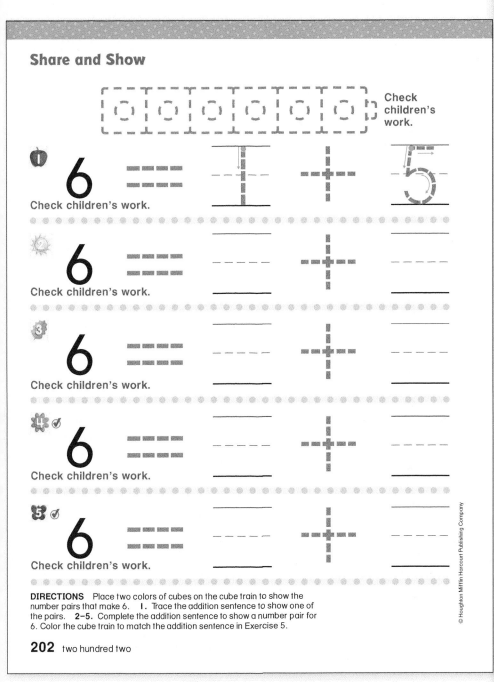

Check children's work.

1 6 = $\square$ | + 5

Check children's work.

2 6 = $\square$ +

Check children's work.

3 6 = $\square$ +

Check children's work.

4 6 = $\square$ +

Check children's work.

5 6 = $\square$ +

DIRECTIONS Place two colors of cubes on the cube train to show the number pairs that make 6. **1.** Trace the addition sentence to show one of the pairs. **2–5.** Complete the addition sentence to show a number pair for 6. Color the cube train to match the addition sentence in Exercise 5.

202 two hundred two

© Houghton Mifflin Harcourt Publishing Company

 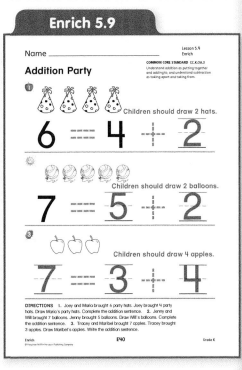
---

③ PRACTICE Math Board

▶ Share and Show • Guided Practice

For Exercise 1, have children use connecting cubes to model a number pair that makes 6, namely, 1 and 5. Then have them trace the addition sentence and model the number pair.

For Exercises 2 through 5, children model number pairs for 6 and complete addition sentences. Have children share number pairs that make 6 and discuss why more than one number pair is possible.

After the discussion, have children color the cube train to match the addition sentence they wrote for Exercise 5.

Use Exercises 4 and 5 for Quick Check.

⚠ COMMON ERRORS

Error Children may not correctly record the cube train they made.

Example For Exercise 2, children make a cube train with four red and two yellow cubes but record 1 + 5.

Springboard to Learning After children model the number pair, tell them to count all of one color and write that number in the addition sentence. Then repeat for the other color.

Lesson 5.9   202

▶ More Practice

Explain to children that they will work with seven-cube trains on this page.

Guide children through Exercise 6.

- **Use red and blue cubes on the cube train to show a pair of numbers that make 7. Complete the addition sentence.**

Have children share their number pairs.

For Exercises 7 through 10, children use cubes to show other number pairs that make 7 and write addition sentences to record their work. Tell them that each number pair should be different than the others. Have children share their number pairs and discuss why there is more than one number pair that can make 7. Have children color the cube train to match the addition sentence they wrote for Exercise 10.

H.O.T. Problem Two children are asked to find a number pair that makes 7. They get two different answers. Can they both be correct? Explain.

- **How many number pairs are there for the number 7?** 8

Go Deeper

Children should be able to explain that there are many number pairs for 7. One child may show 7 = 5 + 2 and another child may show 7 = 3 + 4. Both answers are correct because they both make 7.

Name _____

Check children's work.

6 7 ____ ____ | __+__ ____
Check children's work.

7 7 ____ ____ | __+__ ____
Check children's work.

8 7 ____ ____ | __+__ ____
Check children's work.

9 7 ____ ____ | __+__ ____
Check children's work.

10 7 ____ ____ | __+__ ____
Check children's work.

© Houghton Mifflin Harcourt Publishing Company

DIRECTIONS Place two colors of cubes on the cube train to show the number pairs that make 7. **6–10.** Complete the addition sentence to show a number pair for 7. Color the cube train to match the addition sentence in Exercise 10.

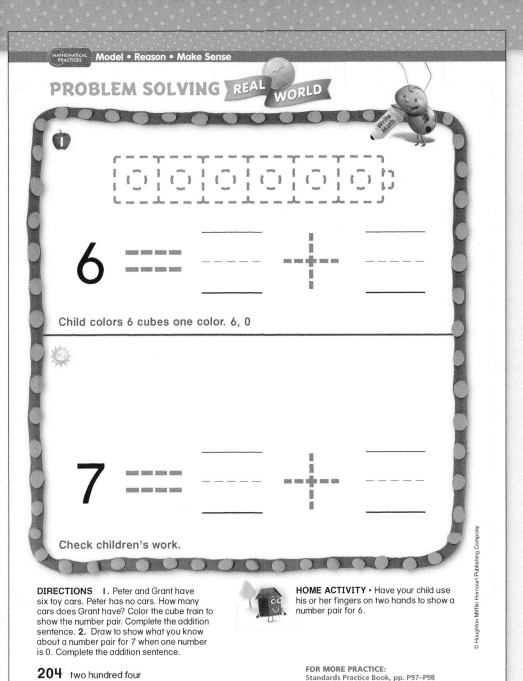

PROBLEM SOLVING REAL WORLD

6 === ___ + ___

Child colors 6 cubes one color. 6, 0

7 === ___ + ___

Check children's work.

DIRECTIONS 1. Peter and Grant have six toy cars. Peter has no cars. How many cars does Grant have? Color the cube train to show the number pair. Complete the addition sentence. **2.** Draw to show what you know about a number pair for 7 when one number is 0. Complete the addition sentence.

 HOME ACTIVITY • Have your child use his or her fingers on two hands to show a number pair for 6.

204 two hundred four

FOR MORE PRACTICE:
Standards Practice Book, pp. P97–P98

© Houghton Mifflin Harcourt Publishing Company

▶ **Problem Solving**

For Exercise 1, read the addition word problem.

Peter and Grant have six toy cars. Peter has no cars. How many cars does Grant have?

• **How many cars does Peter have?** 0
• **If Peter has no cars and they have six cars in all, how many cars does Grant have?** 6

Have children color the cube train to model the problem and find the answer. Discuss how they knew that Grant has six cars.
Possible answer: The total is 6 and Peter has no cars, so Grant must have all six cars.

For Exercise 2, ask children to show what they know about a number pair that makes 7 when one of the numbers is 0.

 Have children take turns explaining their work.

4 SUMMARIZE MATHEMATICAL PRACTICES

Essential Question

How can you model and write addition sentences for number pairs for each sum of 6 and 7? I can make a set of cubes in one color and make a set in a different color until I have 6 or 7. Then I can fill in the numbers I used to write the addition sentence.

Differentiated Instruction INDEPENDENT ACTIVITIES

Grab-and-Go! Differentiated Centers Kit

Activities
Sensational Seven
Children complete the orange Activity Card 15 by modeling the number 7 using two groups of objects.

Literature
Flowers for Flossie
Children read the book and count and add flowers of different colors.

Games
Spin to Add
Children use connecting cubes to model addition problems.

Digital Path

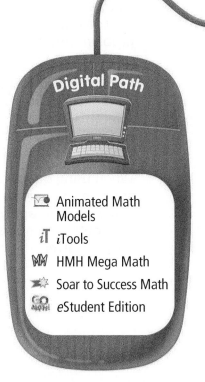

- Animated Math Models
- iTools
- HMH Mega Math
- Soar to Success Math
- eStudent Edition

Hands On: Algebra • Number Pairs for 8

LESSON AT A GLANCE

Common Core Standard

Understand addition as putting together and adding to, and understand subtraction as taking apart and taking from.

CC.K.OA.3 Decompose numbers less than or equal to 10 into pairs in more than one way, e.g., by using objects or drawings, and record each decomposition by a drawing or equation (e.g., 5 = 2 + 3 and 5 = 4 + 1).

Also CC.K.OA.1, CC.K.OA.2

Lesson Objective

Decompose 8 into pairs in more than one way and record each decomposition with an equation.

Essential Question

How can you model and write addition sentences for number pairs for sums of 8?

Materials

MathBoard, connecting cubes

Digital Path

🖥 **Animated Math Models**   iT *i*Tools: Counters

🔲 **eStudent Edition**

PROFESSIONAL DEVELOPMENT
Building Mathematical Practices

CC.K–12.MP.2 Reason abstractly and quantitatively.

As children become more mathematically proficient, they start to understand quantities and their relationships in problem situations.

Children will be able to decontextualize. They will eventually represent the problems abstractly and symbolically without necessarily using the specific referents. They will also develop the ability to contextualize, to pause as needed while filling in the referents for the symbols involved.

When using quantitative reasoning, children learn to create a coherent representation of the problem. They will be able to apply this in this lesson because they will manipulate numbers within the symbolic representation they are given.

Daily Routines

Common Core

Problem of the Day

Number of the Day Tap your foot eight times. Snap your fingers eight times. Hold up eight fingers.

Have the children tell you what they know about the number 8.

Fluency Builder

Counting Tape

Materials Counting Tape

Continue to update daily. Choose discussion questions based on the numbers on your counting Tape to continue developing number sense. For example:

- **How is the number 61 different from 81?**
- **What is the same about 61 and 81?**
- **Which number is greater, 67 or 74? Why?**
- **Which number is 1 greater than 18? Which is 1 less than 18?**
- **Find today's mystery number. It comes right after 35. It is a neighbor of 37. It has 3 groups of tens and 6 leftover ones.**
- **Can you convince us of your answer using math talk?**

73 74 75 76 77 78 79 80 81

Differentiated Instruction Activities

ELL Language Support
 Kinesthetic
Individual / Small Group

Strategy: Restate

Materials red and blue crayons

Restating key vocabulary helps students understand math problems.

- On the board write **8 = 5 + 3**. Tell children that this addition sentence says 8 is equal to 5 plus 3.

- Then say that another way. **8 is the same as 5 and 3.** Help students see the correspondence between *is equal to* and *is the same as* and between *plus* and *and*.

Repeat with other number sentences, such as 6 = 4 + 2.

See **ELL** Activity Guide for leveled activities.

Enrich
 Kinesthetic / Partners

Materials connecting cubes, Numeral Cards (0–7), (8–15) (see *eTeacher Resources*), drawing of blank eight-cube train

Carlos has an eight-cube train. It has some red and some blue cubes. How many cubes of each color could the cube train have?

- Provide partners with a drawing of a blank eight-cube train. Give each partner a different color of cubes. Place cards facedown.

- One partner draws a card from 0 to 8 and places that number of red cubes on the cube train. The other partner places enough blue cubes on the cube train to make 8. That partner writes the addition sentence to show 8.

- Have children put the card aside and repeat the activity until they find all the ways to show 8.

 RtI Response to Intervention

Reteach Tier 1
 Kinesthetic / Visual
Whole Class / Small Group

Materials connecting cubes

Children will find number pairs for 8.

Tim has eight cubes in a basket. Some are red and some are yellow. How many cubes could he have of each color?

- Ask children to use the cubes to model 8 as many ways as they can. Suggest that they start with 1 + 7 and then change one cube at a time.

- Guide children to record the addition sentences in order to help them see the ways they have already recorded.

- **So how many cubes could Tim have of each color?** Some possible answers: 1 red 7 yellow, 2 red 6 yellow, 3 red 5 yellow, 4 red 4 yellow

Tier 2
 Visual / Kinesthetic
Small Group

Materials connecting cubes

Children will find number pairs for 8.

Marie has eight cubes. Some are red and some are yellow. How many of each color could she have?

- Have children place eight red cubes in a row. Have them check that there are 8 in all. Write 8 and 0.

- Ask children to replace one red cube with a yellow cube. Ask what number pair the cubes show. 1 and 7

- Continue to have children replace another red cube each time and record each new number pair.

- Discuss why there are several number pairs for this problem.

1 ENGAGE

Materials connecting cubes, two clear bowls

Access Prior Knowledge Write 7 on the board. Show seven yellow cubes in one bowl and seven orange cubes in the other bowl. Remove six or fewer cubes from one bowl. Count the cubes aloud with children.

Remove additional cubes from the other bowl to make the sum of 7. Count the cubes aloud with children. After children see there are seven cubes in all, call a volunteer to complete an addition sentence on the board.

As you continue the activity, be sure to include a number pair with a zero.

- **What would the addition sentence be if I removed seven cubes from one bowl and none or zero cubes from the other bowl?**
  $7 = 7 + 0$ or $7 = 0 + 7$

2 TEACH and TALK GO Online Animated Math Models

▶ **Listen and Draw**

Materials connecting cubes

Read this addition word problem to children.

Lisa used yellow and orange cubes to make an eight-cube train. How many yellow cubes and how many orange cubes could she have used?

- **What information is given in the problem?**
  Lisa used eight yellow and orange cubes to make a cube train.

- **What does the problem ask you to find?**
  how many yellow cubes and how many orange cubes Lisa could have used

Read the addition sentence aloud with children. Have them use yellow and orange cubes to model the addition sentence and then color the cube train to match. Ask children to trace the addition sentence, including the *is equal to* and *plus* symbols.
$8 = 7 + 1$

- **Is this the only way you can show 8? Explain.** No. Possible answer: There are other number pairs to make 8. $6 + 2$, $5 + 3$, $4 + 4$

- **Why are there different ways to show 8?**
  Possible answer: There are different numbers that when put together make 8 in all.

 COMMON CORE

CC.K.OA.3 Decompose numbers less than or equal to 10 into pairs in more than one way, e.g., by using objects or drawings, and record each decomposition by a drawing or equation (e.g., $5 = 2 + 3$ and $5 = 4 + 1$).

Name _____

Algebra • Number Pairs for 8

HANDS ON Lesson 5.10

Essential Question How can you model and write addition sentences for number pairs for sums of 8?

COMMON CORE STANDARD CC.K.OA.3
Understand addition as putting together and adding to, and understand subtraction as taking apart and taking from.

Listen and Draw

DIRECTIONS Use two colors of cubes to make a cube train to match the addition sentence. Color the cube train to show your work. Trace the addition sentence.

Check children's work.

Chapter 5 • Lesson 10

two hundred five **205**

Standards Practice 5.10 **Common Core** SPIRAL REVIEW

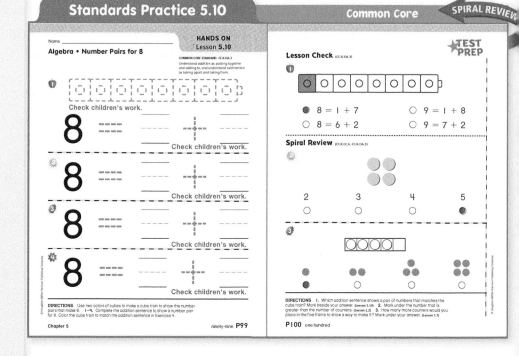

DIRECTIONS Use two colors of cubes to make a cube train to show the number pairs that make 8. 1–4. Complete the addition sentence to show a number pair for 8. Color the cube train to match the addition sentence in Exercise 4.

Chapter 5

ninety-nine **P99**

Lesson Check (CC.K.OA.3)

① ● $8 = 1 + 7$ ○ $9 = 1 + 8$
  ○ $8 = 6 + 2$ ○ $9 = 7 + 2$

Spiral Review (CC.K.CC.6, CC.K.OA.3)

DIRECTIONS 1. Which addition sentence shows a pair of numbers that matches the cube train? Mark beside your answer. (Lesson 5.10) 2. Mark under the number that is greater than the number of counters. (Lesson 2.2) 3. How many more counters would you place in the five frame to show a way to make 5? Mark under your answer. (Lesson 1.7)

P100 one hundred

Share and Show

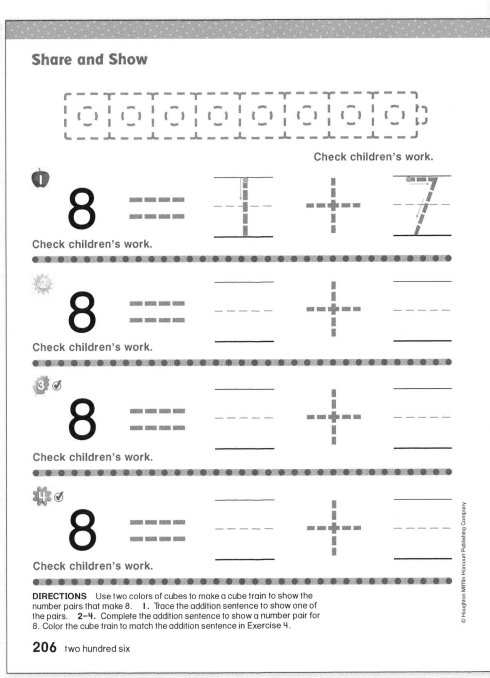

Check children's work.

1 8 = ⬜ I + 7

Check children's work.

2 8 = ⬜ ___ + ___

Check children's work.

3 ✓ 8 = ⬜ ___ + ___

Check children's work.

4 ✓ 8 = ⬜ ___ + ___

Check children's work.

DIRECTIONS Use two colors of cubes to make a cube train to show the number pairs that make 8. **1.** Trace the addition sentence to show one of the pairs. **2–4.** Complete the addition sentence to show a number pair for 8. Color the cube train to match the addition sentence in Exercise 4.

206 two hundred six

© Houghton Mifflin Harcourt Publishing Company

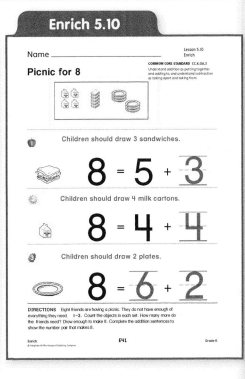
---

③ PRACTICE

▶ **Share and Show** • **Guided Practice**

Have children find Exercise 1.

- **Use connecting cubes to model a number pair that makes 8. Then trace the first addition sentence to find one number pair.**
  8 = 1 + 7

For Exercises 2 through 4, ask children to model other ways to make 8 with cubes and to complete an addition sentence for each one.

- **Will there be more than one number pair? Explain.** Yes. There are many number pairs that make 8.

Explain that all the addition sentences must use different number pairs. When children finish Exercise 4, ask them to share their number pairs. Then have them color the cube train to match their addition sentence for Exercise 4.

Use Exercises 3 and 4 for Quick Check.

✓ Quick Check ▲ RtI

If a child misses Exercise 3 and 4

Then Differentiate Instruction with
- RtI Tier 1 Activity, p. 205B
- Reteach 5.10
- Soar to Success Math 10.09

⚠ COMMON ERRORS

Error Children write the same addition sentence for all problems.

Example In Exercises 2 through 4, children repeat 8 = 1 + 7.

Springboard to Learning Have children check each addition sentence they complete to be sure that it matches the cube train they made and that it is different than their other number pairs.

▶ More Practice

For Exercises 5 through 7, explain that children will continue their work with 8. Tell them to use different number pairs than they used on the previous page. If there is time, have children share their number pairs. Finally, have them color the cube train to match their addition sentence for Exercise 7.

H.O.T. Problem When you find a number pair that makes 8, you can usually make another number pair by showing the same numbers in a different order. When would you not be able to make a second number pair by using the same numbers in different order?

• **Write that number pair.** 4 and 4

Go Deeper

Allow children time to think about different number pairs that make 8. Invite discussion and have children share their thinking. Children should see that when the two numbers in the number pair are the same, such as 4 + 4, there is only one number pair with those numbers, so they cannot make a second number pair using the same numbers in different order.

Name _____

Check children's work.

5

8 === ____ + ____
____ ____

Check children's work.

6

8 === ____ + ____
____ ____

Check children's work.

7

8 === ____ + ____
____ ____

Check children's work.

DIRECTIONS Use two colors of cubes to make a cube train to show the number pairs that make 8. **5–7.** Complete the addition sentence to show a number pair for 8. Color the cube train to match the addition sentence in Exercise 7.

© Houghton Mifflin Harcourt Publishing Company

Chapter 5 • Lesson 10   two hundred seven **207**

Cross-Curricular

SCIENCE

• Have children draw two sets of one to four flowers.
• Ask children to share what they know about flowers. Have children tell how flowers are the same and different than each other. Elicit that flowers grow and that they need water.
• Ask children to tell an addition word problem about the sets of flowers that they drew.
• Then ask children to tell an addition sentence using numbers and symbols.

SOCIAL STUDIES

Materials Number and Symbol Tiles (front) (see *eTeacher Resources*), crayons

• Remind children that some of the goods or items people use are made by people who work in factories.
• Point out that crayons are made in factories. Name some other things in the classroom that are made in factories.
• Show two sets of crayons. Have children use their number tiles and symbol tiles to make an addition sentence about the sets of crayons.

PROBLEM SOLVING REAL WORLD

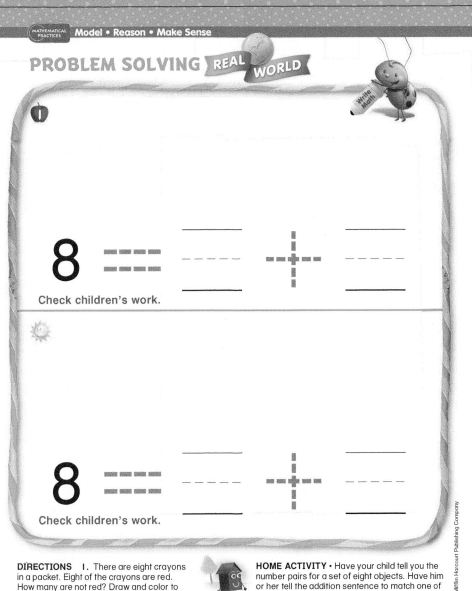

8 === ___ ___ + ___

___ ___

Check children's work.

8 === ___ ___ + ___

___ ___

Check children's work.

© Houghton Mifflin Harcourt Publishing Company

DIRECTIONS **1.** There are eight crayons in a packet. Eight of the crayons are red. How many are not red? Draw and color to show how you solved. Complete the addition sentence. **2.** Draw to show what you know about a different number pair for 8. Complete the addition sentence.

HOME ACTIVITY • Have your child tell you the number pairs for a set of eight objects. Have him or her tell the addition sentence to match one of the number pairs.

208 two hundred eight

FOR MORE PRACTICE:
Standards Practice Book, pp. P99–P100

▶ **Problem Solving** (MATHEMATICAL PRACTICES)

Read the addition word problem aloud in Exercise 1. Be sure children understand that there are eight crayons in all.

- **How many are red?** 8
- **If there are eight crayons, and eight are red, how many are not red?** 0
- **Draw and color to show how you solved the problem. What numbers are in the number pair?** 8 and 0 **Complete the addition sentence.**
- **When you add zero to a number, does the number change?** No. The number stays the same.

For Exercise 2, ask children to draw to show what they know about a number pair for 8. Have children complete the addition sentence.

 Have children share and explain their drawings and number sentences to classmates.

4 SUMMARIZE (MATHEMATICAL PRACTICES)

Essential Question

How can you model and write addition sentences for number pairs for sums of 8? I can make a set of cubes in one color and make a set in a different color until I have 8. Then I can fill in the numbers I used to write the addition sentence.

Differentiated Instruction — INDEPENDENT ACTIVITIES

Grab-and-Go!
Differentiated Centers Kit

Activities
All Together Now!

 Children complete the purple Activity Card 6 by using two-color counters in combinations that add up to 9.

Literature
Flowers for Flossie

 Children read the book and count and add flowers of different colors.

Games
Spin to Add

Children use connecting cubes to model addition problems.

Digital Path

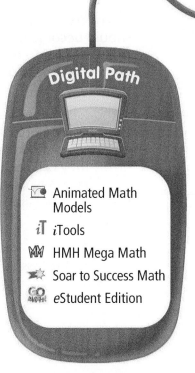

- Animated Math Models
- iTools
- HMH Mega Math
- Soar to Success Math
- eStudent Edition

Hands On: Algebra • Number Pairs for 9

LESSON AT A GLANCE

Common Core Standard

Understand addition as putting together and adding to, and understand subtraction as taking apart and taking from.

CC.K.OA.3 Decompose numbers less than or equal to 10 into pairs in more than one way, e.g., by using objects or drawings, and record each decomposition by a drawing or equation (e.g., 5 = 2 + 3 and 5 = 4 + 1).

Also CC.K.OA.1, CC.K.OA.2

Lesson Objective

Decompose 9 into pairs in more than one way and record each decomposition with an equation.

Essential Question

How can you model and write addition sentences for number pairs for sums of 9?

Materials

MathBoard, connecting cubes

Digital Path

☑ Animated Math Models   iT *iTools:* Counters

☑ *eStudent Edition*

 PROFESSIONAL DEVELOPMENT **About the Math**
COMMON CORE

Teaching for Depth

As children work their way through this chapter, they should become more familiar with strategies to use to find number pairs to make a given number, such as: reverse the pair order, trade cube colors one cube at a time, and use a pattern.

Although children are not asked specifically to find all the combinations, they should realize that when they use a pattern to find the number pairs, rather than trial and error, they can be sure they have found all the possible pairs. You may wish to have a discussion on how the number of possible combinations relates to the given number.

📱 **Professional Development Video Podcasts**
PODCASTING

Daily Routines
Math Board

Common Core
SPIRAL REVIEW

Problem of the Day
eTransparency
5.11

Number of the Day What number is one less than 5?
What number is one more than 5?
What can you tell about the number 5?

4; 6; Possible answers: It is greater than 4; I can count from 1 to 5.

Have children tell you what a five frame and ten frame would look like with five counters in it.

Fluency Builder

Number Pairs to 8

Write a number that is 8 or less on the board. Ask children to name number pairs for the number.

Record each answer on the board. Ask for more pairs until all possible number pairs have been named.

Continue with 7, 6, and 5 as time allows.

Have children compare the number of ways to make each number pair for the given number.

Differentiated Instruction Activities

 Language Support Kinesthetic / Small Group

Strategy: Model Concepts

Materials connecting cubes

Children may understand word problems and vocabulary if they are modeled.

- **Adam has nine cubes. Some are red and some are blue. How many red cubes and how many blue cubes could he have?**

- Read and model the word problem step by step using cubes.

- Lead children to see that you can use models to solve a problem.

See **ELL** Activity Guide for leveled activities.

Enrich Kinesthetic / Partners

Materials plastic cups, two-color counters

Give partners two cups and nine counters.

- Have the first child separate nine counters into two cups. Then have him or her give one cup to the second child while keeping the mystery cup.

- Have the second child count the counters in the cup and then guess the number of counters in the mystery cup.

- Have the first child reveal the counters in the mystery cup to check.

- Have both partners use that number pair that makes 9 to complete an addition sentence.

- Partners switch roles and repeat the activity.

 RtI Response to Intervention

Reteach Tier 1 Kinesthetic / Visual / Whole Class / Small Group

Materials connecting cubes

Guide children to use a pattern to find number pairs for 9.

- Have them make a cube train with nine red cubes. **How many red cubes are there?** 9 **How many blue cubes are there?** 0 Have children complete an addition sentence for the number pair, $9 = 9 + 0$.

- Have them replace one red cube with one blue cube. **How many red cubes are there?** 8 **How many blue cubes are there?** 1 Have children complete an addition sentence for the number pair, $9 = 8 + 1$.

- Continue guiding children to replace one red cube with one blue cube in the cube train until all of the pairs have been made.

Tier 2 Visual / Kinesthetic / Small Group

Materials two-color counters, paper cup

Children will find number pairs for 9.

- Gather children in a circle around a table.

- Write $9 = \underline{\quad} + \underline{\quad}$ on paper that you have titled "Number Pairs for 9."

- Count out nine counters with children and place them in a cup.

- **How many counters are in the cup?** 9

- Gently shake and pour the counters on the table.

- **How many red counters are there?**

- **How many yellow counters are there?**

- Record the pair of numbers to complete the addition sentence.

- Repeat the activity, having different children shake and pour the counters.

① ENGAGE iTools Online

Materials iTools: Counters

Access Prior Knowledge Review the number and numeral 9. Ask children to count aloud as you stamp 9 counters of your choice on the mat. Then have children record the numeral 9 on paper. Repeat the activity inviting different volunteers to stamp out nine counters of their choice.

② TEACH and TALK GO Online Animated Math Models

▶ **Listen and Draw** MATHEMATICAL PRACTICES

Materials connecting cubes

Ask children to listen carefully as you read the following problem aloud.

Ari made a nine-cube train. Some cubes are orange and some are green. How many orange cubes and how many green cubes could he have?

Read the addition sentence with children and have children model it with cubes.

- **How many cubes are in the cube train?** 9

Have children count to check that they have nine cubes in their cube trains.

- **How many orange cubes are there?** 8
- **How many green cubes are there?** 1

Have children color the cube train on the page to match their cube trains and then trace the numbers and symbols to complete the addition sentence.

- **Do you think there are other ways Ari could have made his cube train? Explain.** Yes. There are other number pairs that make 9.

COMMON CORE

CC.K.OA.3 Decompose numbers less than or equal to 10 into pairs in more than one way, e.g., by using objects or drawings, and record each decomposition by a drawing or equation (e.g., 5 = 2 + 3 and 5 = 4 + 1).

Name _____

Algebra • Number Pairs for 9

HANDS ON
Lesson 5.11

Essential Question How can you model and write addition sentences for number pairs for sums of 9?

COMMON CORE STANDARD CC.K.OA.3
Understand addition as putting together and adding to, and understand subtraction as taking apart and taking from.

Listen and Draw

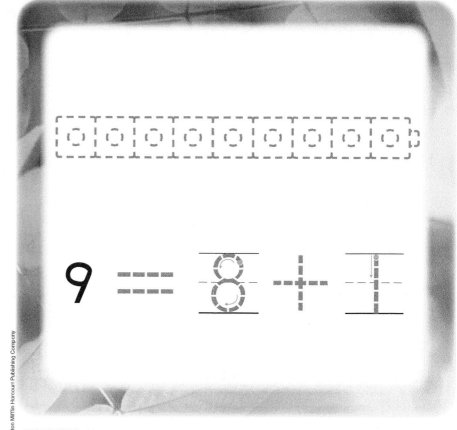

$$9 = 8 + 1$$

DIRECTIONS Use two colors of cubes to make a cube train to match the addition sentence. Color the cube train to show your work. Trace the addition sentence.

Check children's work.

Chapter 5 • Lesson 11

two hundred nine **209**

Standards Practice 5.11

Common Core   SPIRAL REVIEW

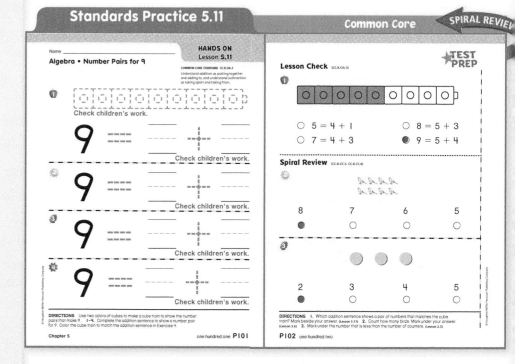

Name _____

Algebra • Number Pairs for 9

HANDS ON
Lesson 5.11

COMMON CORE STANDARD CC.K.OA.3
Understand addition as putting together and adding to, and understand subtraction as taking apart and taking from.

Lesson Check (CC.K.OA.3)

TEST PREP

○ 5 = 4 + 1   ○ 8 = 5 + 3
○ 7 = 4 + 3   ● 9 = 5 + 4

Spiral Review (CC.K.CC.3, CC.K.CC.6)

8   7   6   5
●   ○   ○   ○

2   3   4   5
●   ○   ○   ○

DIRECTIONS 1. Which addition sentence shows a pair of numbers that matches the cube train? Mark beside your answer. (Lesson 5.11) 2. Count how many birds. Mark under your answer. (Lesson 3.6) 3. Mark under the number that is less than the number of counters. (Lesson 2.3)

P102 one hundred two

DIRECTIONS Use two colors of cubes to make a cube train to show the number pairs that make 9. 1–4. Complete the addition sentence to show a number pair for 9. Color the cube train to match the addition sentence in Exercise 4.

Chapter 5   one hundred one P101

Share and Show

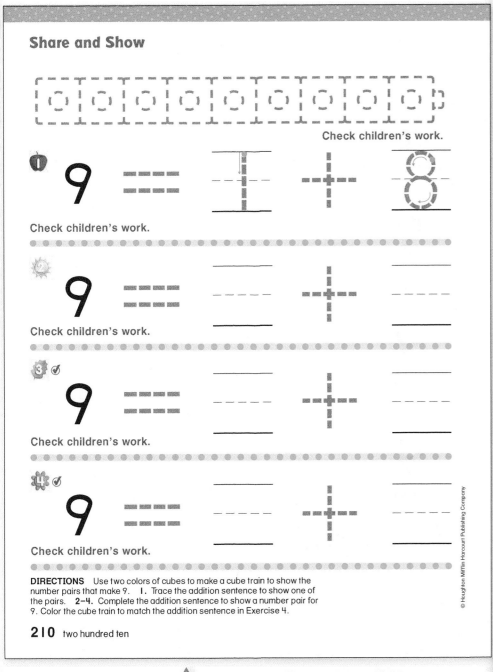

Check children's work.

① $9 = \boxed{1} + \boxed{8}$

Check children's work.

② $9 = \_\_ + \_\_$

Check children's work.

③ ✓ $9 = \_\_ + \_\_$

Check children's work.

④ ✓ $9 = \_\_ + \_\_$

Check children's work.

DIRECTIONS Use two colors of cubes to make a cube train to show the number pairs that make 9. **1.** Trace the addition sentence to show one of the pairs. **2–4.** Complete the addition sentence to show a number pair for 9. Color the cube train to match the addition sentence in Exercise 4.

210 two hundred ten

© Houghton Mifflin Harcourt Publishing Company

---

③ PRACTICE Math Board

▶ **Share and Show** • Guided Practice

- **Find Exercise 1. Use connecting cubes to model a number pair that makes 9. Then trace the first addition sentence to find one number pair.** $9 = 1 + 8$

For Exercises 2 through 4, have children model other ways to make 9 with cubes and complete an addition sentence for each one. Explain that all the addition sentences must use different number pairs. When children finish Exercise 4, ask them to share their number pairs. Then have them color the cube train to match their addition sentence for Exercise 4.

Use Exercises 3 and 4 for Quick Check.

> ✓ **Quick Check** ▲ RtI
>
> **If** a child misses Exercise 3 and 4
>
> **Then** Differentiate Instruction with
> - RtI Tier 1 Activity, p. 209B
> - Reteach 5.11
> - Soar to Success Math 10.09

> ⚠ **COMMON ERRORS**
>
> **Error** Children may put more than or fewer than nine cubes on the cube train.
>
> **Example** Children place eight cubes on the cube train.
>
> **Springboard to Learning** Have children count to make sure they have nine cubes in all before recording a number sentence.

Lesson 5.11 210

► More Practice

For Exercises 5 through 8, tell children that they will continue their work with 9. Remind them to model with connecting cubes and to use different number pairs than they used on the previous page to solve the problem. If there is time, have children share their number pairs. Finally, have them color the cube train to match their addition sentence for Exercise 8.

H.O.T. Problem How can you know which number pairs you have used and which you have not used?

Go Deeper

Have children look back at their completed student pages. Ask volunteers to explain how they found a different number pair for each addition sentence. Possible answer: I can start with one cube of one color and the rest of the cubes a different color. Then for each new model, I add one cube of the first color and take away one cube of the other color.

Then list the numbers 1 to 9 on the board.

For each number in order ask,

• **1 and what number makes 9?** 8

Continue in this manner until all the number pairs for 9 are listed.

How can you explain this list of number pairs for 9? Possible answer: One number in each pair gets larger by 1 and the other number gets smaller by 1.

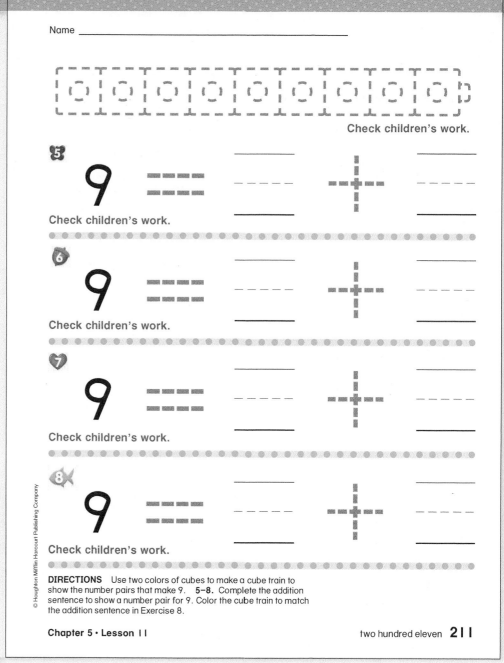

DIRECTIONS Use two colors of cubes to make a cube train to show the number pairs that make 9. **5–8.** Complete the addition sentence to show a number pair for 9. Color the cube train to match the addition sentence in Exercise 8.

Chapter 5 • Lesson 11   two hundred eleven **211**

COMMON CORE PROFESSIONAL DEVELOPMENT

Math Talk in Action

As children complete Exercises 4 through 8, discuss reversing number pairs to find new ways to make 9.

Teacher: In Exercise 4, how many cubes of one color did you show first?

Michael: Five cubes.

Teacher: How many cubes of the other color did you show?

Michael: Four cubes.

Teacher: So the numbers 5 and 4 make 9.

Michael: Yes.

Teacher: What happens if you flip or turn your train around? Try it.

Teacher: Now how many cubes of one color does your model show first?

Michael: Four cubes.

Teacher: How many cubes of the other color does your model show?

Michael: Five cubes.

Teacher: Is this another way to show 9?

Michael: Yes, because the two numbers are in a different order.

Teacher: How does knowing this help you find more ways to make 9?

Michael: I can change the order of two numbers I know make 9 and get another way to make 9.

Teacher: Great discovery, Michael!

PROBLEM SOLVING REAL WORLD

①

9 == ____ ____ + ____ ____

Check children's work.

9 == ____ ____ + ____ ____

Check children's work.

DIRECTIONS 1. Shelby has nine friends. None of them are boys. How many are girls? Complete the addition sentence to show the number pair. 2. Draw to show what you know about a different number pair for 9. Complete the addition sentence.

212 two hundred twelve

HOME ACTIVITY • Have your child use his or her fingers on two hands to show a number pair for 9.

© Houghton Mifflin Harcourt Publishing Company

FOR MORE PRACTICE:
Standards Practice Book, pp. P101–P102

▶ ## Problem Solving MATHEMATICAL PRACTICES

For Exercise 1, ask children to listen carefully as you read aloud the following problem. Have them model with cubes.

Shelby has nine friends. None of them are boys. How many are girls?

- **How many friends does Shelby have in all?** 9 **How many are boys?** none
- **What number do you know stands for *none*?** 0
- **If there are zero boys, how many are girls?** 9

Have children complete the addition sentence to solve the problem.

For Exercise 2, ask children to draw a picture that shows a different number pair for 9 and then complete the addition sentence to match it.

 Have children explain what they know about a number pair for 9.

④ SUMMARIZE MATHEMATICAL PRACTICES

Essential Question

How can you model and write addition sentences for number pairs for sums of 9? I can make a set of cubes in one color and make a set in a different color that make 9 in all. Then I can fill in the numbers I used to write the addition sentence.

Differentiated Instruction
INDEPENDENT ACTIVITIES

Grab-and-Go!
Differentiated Centers Kit

Activities
All Together Now!

 Children complete the purple Activity Card 6 by using two-color counters in combinations that add up to 9.

Literature
Flowers for Flossie

 Children read the book and count and add flowers of different colors.

Games
Spin to Add

Children use connecting cubes to model addition problems.

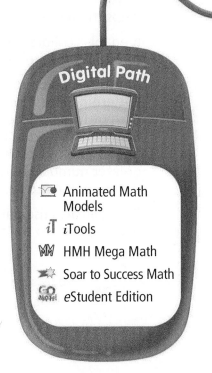

Digital Path

- Animated Math Models
- iTools
- HMH Mega Math
- Soar to Success Math
- eStudent Edition

Hands On: Algebra • Number Pairs for 10

LESSON AT A GLANCE

Common Core Standard
Understand addition as putting together and adding to, and understand subtraction as taking apart and taking from.
CC.K.OA.3 Decompose numbers less than or equal to 10 into pairs in more than one way, e.g., by using objects or drawings, and record each decomposition by a drawing or equation (e.g., $5 = 2 + 3$ and $5 = 4 + 1$).

Also CC.K.OA.1, CC.K.OA.2

Lesson Objective
Decompose 10 into pairs in more than one way and record each decomposition with an equation.

Essential Question
How can you model and write addition sentences for number pairs for sums of 10?

Materials
MathBoard, connecting cubes

Digital Path

-  Animated Math Models
- iT *i*Tools: Counters
- HMH Mega Math
- eStudent Edition

COMMON CORE PROFESSIONAL DEVELOPMENT

About the Math

Why Teach This

Teaching children how to make pairs for a given number helps them build a foundation for mathematics.

It enables children to see how there can be more than one solution for a problem.

It provides an opportunity for children to discover patterning and how it can help them solve problems. Each of these will be used as children learn more complex mathematical skills. For example, they will use more than one solution when learning about how to represent greater numbers using place value and when they show different ways to represent the same amount of money.

They will also use patterning with numbers and shapes in upper grades to build a solid foundation for algebra.

PODCASTING Professional Development Video Podcasts

Daily Routines
Common Core

Math Board

SPIRAL REVIEW

Problem of the Day

eTransparency 5.12

Word of the Day What number is one less than 3?
What number is one less than 7?
What number is one less than 10?
2; 6; 9
Review the meaning of *less than* and give more problems with other numbers.

Fluency Builder

Materials Addition Fact Cards (within 5) (see *eTeacher Resources*)

Add Within 5

Have one child come to the front of the room. Have another child join him or her.

How many children came first? 1 **How many children came next?** 1 Have children complete an addition sentence, $1 + 1 = 2$.

Have two more children join them.

How many children were there first? 2 **How many more children came?** 2 Have children complete an addition sentence, $2 + 2 = 4$.

Show addition fact cards for $1 + 1$ and $2 + 2$.

Ask children to state the sums for each fact. $1 + 1 = 2, 2 + 2 = 4$

Differentiated Instruction Activities

ELL Language Support
 Visual / Linguistic
Small Group

Strategy: Describe

Materials connecting cubes

Children can practice their comprehension by describing in words what they see. Make the following model for children with cubes.

- For each train in the model ask children to describe how it shows a number pair for 10.

- Then have them study the whole model and ask children to describe what they see.

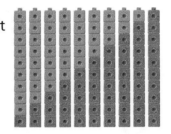

See **ELL** Activity Guide for leveled activities.

Enrich
 Visual
Individual / Partners

Materials Workmat 3 (ten frame) (see *eTeacher Resources*), stapler

Make and give partners multiple copies of ten frames.

- Have them work together to color in each ten frame to show a different number pair for 10.

- Have them record the matching addition sentence beneath each ten frame.

- Have children put the pages in an order that makes sense.

- Help them bind their pages to make a book.

RtI Response to Intervention

Reteach Tier 1
 Kinesthetic / Visual
Whole Class / Small Group

Materials connecting cubes, Workmat 3 (ten frame) (see *eTeacher Resources*)

Read the problem aloud. **Sid has ten cubes. Some are red and some are yellow. How many red cubes and how many yellow cubes could he have?**

- Record the matching addition sentence. $10 = 9 + 1$

- **Is this the only number pair for the problem? Why or why not?** Possible answer: No. You can have different groups of red and yellow cubes as long as together they make 10.

- At their desks, have children show different ten-cube trains with yellow and red cubes. Then have them count how many of each color and record the matching addition sentence.

- Have children repeat this procedure to find as many number pairs for 10 as they can.

Tier 2
 Kinesthetic / Visual
Small Group

Materials two-color counters, Workmat 3 (ten frame) (see *eTeacher Resources*)

- Write $10 = \_\_\_\_\_ + \_\_\_\_\_$ on the board. Put ten counters on a ten frame, red side up. Have children count to check that they have ten counters on their ten frames.

- Then flip the last counter to its yellow side. Ask children to do the same.

- **How many red counters are there?** 9

- **How many yellow counters are there?** 1

- **This is one number pair that makes 10.**

- Record the matching addition sentence. $10 = 9 + 1$

- Then ask children to flip the second to last counter to its yellow side. Then repeat the questions above. Continue in this fashion until as a group you have modeled and recorded all the numbers pairs for 10.

1 ENGAGE

Materials Workmat 3 (ten frame) (see *eTeacher Resources*), two-color counters

Access Prior Knowledge Use counters on a ten frame to review numbers and numerals 1 to 10. Say a number from 1 to 10 and have children show the number with counters on a ten frame. Remind them to start at the top and fill left to right. Then have them write the matching numeral on their Mathboards.

2 TEACH and TALK GO Online Animated Math Models

▶ **Listen and Draw**

Materials connecting cubes

Read this addition word problem aloud to children.

Su Lin used red and yellow cubes to make a ten-cube train. How many cubes of each color could she have used?

- **What information is given in the problem?**
  Su Lin made a ten-cube train with red and yellow cubes.

- **What do you need to find to solve the problem?** how many red cubes and how many yellow cubes Su Lin could have used

Read the addition sentence aloud with the children. Have them use red and yellow cubes to model the addition sentence and then color the cube train to match. Ask children to trace the addition sentence, including the *is equal to* and *plus* symbols. 10 = 9 + 1

- **Are there other ways you can show 10? If so, name one.** Yes. Possible answers: 6 + 4, 5 + 5, 3 + 7

COMMON CORE CC.K.OA.3 Decompose numbers less than or equal to 10 into pairs in more than one way, e.g., by using objects or drawings, and record each decomposition by a drawing or equation (e.g., 5 = 2 + 3 and 5 = 4 + 1).

Name _____

Algebra • Number Pairs for 10

HANDS ON
Lesson 5.12

Essential Question How can you model and write addition sentences for number pairs for sums of 10?

COMMON CORE STANDARD CC.K.OA.3
Understand addition as putting together and adding to, and understand subtraction as taking apart and taking from.

Listen and Draw

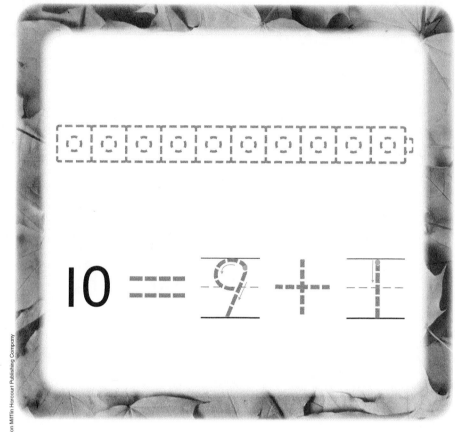

© Houghton Mifflin Harcourt Publishing Company

DIRECTIONS Use two colors of cubes to make a cube train to match the addition sentence. Color the cube train to show your work. Trace the addition sentence.

Chapter 5 • Lesson 12

Check children's work.

two hundred thirteen **213**

Standards Practice 5.12

Common Core SPIRAL REVIEW

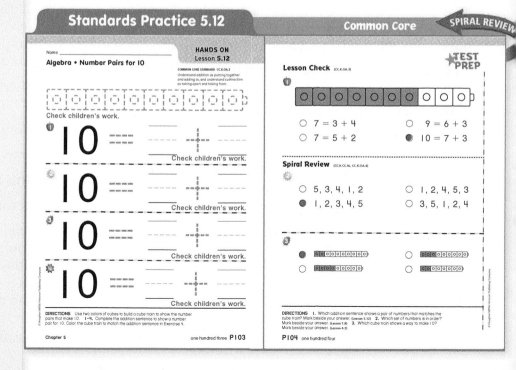

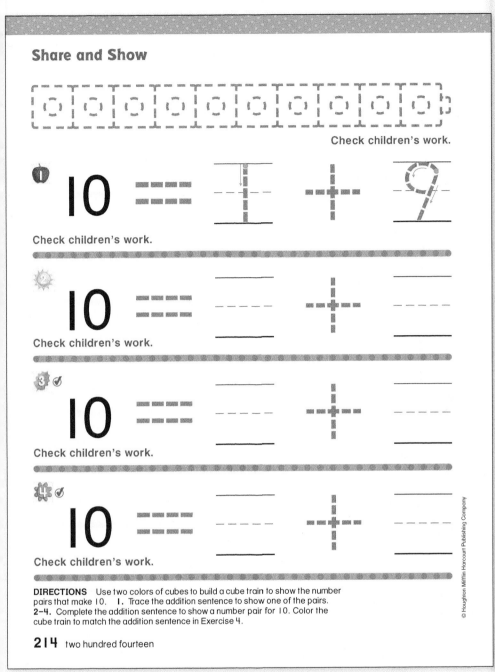

Share and Show

Check children's work.

❶ $10 = 1 + 9$

Check children's work.

❷ $10 = + $

Check children's work.

❸ ✔ $10 = + $

Check children's work.

❹ ✔ $10 = + $

Check children's work.

DIRECTIONS Use two colors of cubes to build a cube train to show the number pairs that make 10. **1.** Trace the addition sentence to show one of the pairs. **2–4.** Complete the addition sentence to show a number pair for 10. Color the cube train to match the addition sentence in Exercise 4.

214 two hundred fourteen

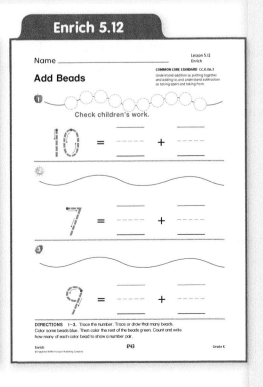

Reteach 5.12

Name _____

Lesson 5.12
Reteach

Algebra • Number Pairs for 10

COMMON CORE STANDARD CC.K.OA.3
Understand addition as putting together and adding to, and understand subtraction as taking apart and taking from.

○○○○○○○○○○

❶ $10 = 1 + 9$

❷ $10 = 2 + 8$

❸ $10 = 3 + 7$

❹ $10 = 4 + 6$

DIRECTIONS Use two-color counters. 1–4. Place ten yellow counters in a row as shown. Look at the gray number. Turn that many counters to red. How many counters are yellow? Trace or write the numbers to show a number pair that makes 10.

Reteach   R43   Grade K
© Houghton Mifflin Harcourt Publishing Company

Enrich 5.12

Name _____

Lesson 5.12
Enrich

Add Beads

COMMON CORE STANDARD CC.K.OA.3
Understand addition as putting together and adding to, and understand subtraction as taking apart and taking from.

❶ Check children's work.

$10 = + $

❷ $7 = + $

❸ $9 = + $

DIRECTIONS 1–3. Trace the number. Trace or draw that many beads. Color some beads blue. Then color the rest of the beads green. Count and write how many of each color bead to show a number pair.

Enrich   E43   Grade K
© Houghton Mifflin Harcourt Publishing Company

---

③ PRACTICE Math Board

▶ **Share and Show • Guided Practice**

For Exercise 1, have children read the addition sentence and then make a cube train with one red cube and nine yellow cubes.

- **Do the numbers 1 and 9 make 10?** yes
  Have children trace the numbers and symbols on their page to complete the addition sentence.

For Exercises 2 through 4, children model other ways to make 10 with cube trains and write an addition sentence for each one. Explain that all the addition sentences must use different number pairs. When children finish Exercise 4, ask them to share their number pairs. Then have them color the cube train to match their addition sentence for Exercise 4.

Use Exercises 3 and 4 for Quick Check.

✔ **Quick Check** RtI

If a child misses Exercise 3 and 4

Then **Differentiate Instruction** with
- RtI Tier 1 Activity, p. 213B
- Reteach 5.12
- ⭐ Soar to Success Math 10.09

⚠ COMMON ERRORS

Error Children may use numbers that do not add to 10 in an addition sentence.

Example For Exercise 3, children write $4 + 5 = 10$.

Springboard to Learning Have children count to check that their cube trains have ten cubes in all. Then have them count the number of each color twice before writing the addition sentence.

► More Practice

For Exercises 5 through 8, explain that children will continue their work with 10. Tell children to build a cube train to show number pairs that make 10. Remind them to use different number pairs than they used on the previous page. If there is time, have children share their number pairs. Have them color the cube train to match their addition sentence for Exercise 8.

H.O.T. Problem What happens if you flip your ten-cube train over? Do you get another way to make 10? Explain your thinking.

Go Deeper

Have children use their cubes to make a ten-cube train and write the number pair they use. Then ask them to flip the train (from left to right) and write the number pair. Discuss why this number pair makes 10. Ask whether anyone did not get a different number pair. Anyone who made a 5 + 5 cube train will not get a different number pair. **Ask the class to explain why the 5 + 5 cube train does not give a different number pair.** Possible answer: The two numbers are the same, so the number pair does not change.

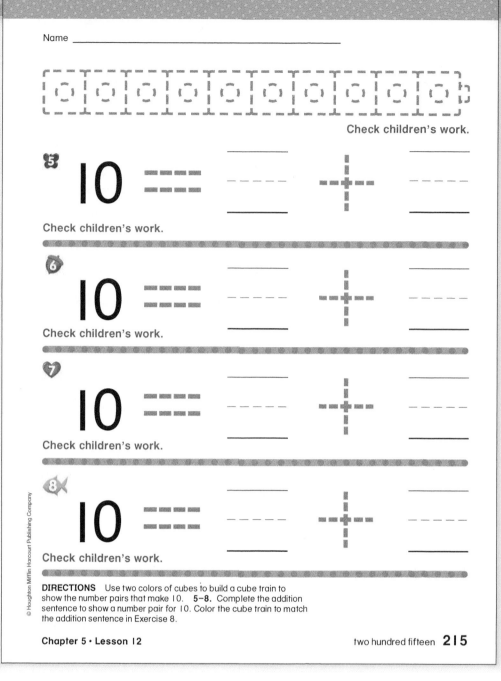

Find All Number Pairs for 10

Investigate Have children create all possible number pairs for 10.

Math Talk

- **What would be the best way to find all the number pairs for 10?** Strategies may vary.

- **How can we find the pairs without using cubes?** Possible answer: Start by using the number we are making for the first pair, 10 and 0. I will use a number one less for the first number and a number one more for the second number for each new number pair to make 10.

- **How will you know when you have all the number pairs?** I will end up with the same numbers I started with for the first pair but in a different order.

Summarize Children will work on finding all possible number pairs for 10.

See if children can verbalize how to find all number pairs without the use of cubes.

Children should demonstrate an understanding of the relationship between the number pairs.

Look for children who are able to communicate a strategy or pattern they are using: for each pair, the first number is one greater and the second number is one less than the previous pair.

PROBLEM SOLVING REAL WORLD

10 = ___ ___ + ___

Check children's work.

10 = ___ ___ + ___

Check children's work.

DIRECTIONS 1. There are ten children in the cafeteria. Ten of them are drinking water. How many children are drinking milk? Complete the addition sentence to show the number pair. 2. Draw to show what you know about a different number pair for 10. Complete the addition sentence.

HOME ACTIVITY • Have your child tell you the number pairs for a set of ten objects. Have him or her tell the addition sentence to match one of the number pairs.

216 two hundred sixteen

FOR EXTRA PRACTICE: Standards Practice Book, p. P106

FOR MORE PRACTICE: Standards Practice Book, pp. P103–P104

© Houghton Mifflin Harcourt Publishing Company

▶ **Problem Solving** MATHEMATICAL PRACTICES

For Exercise 1, ask children to listen carefully as you read aloud the following problem. Encourage them to model with cubes.

There are ten children in the cafeteria. Ten of them are drinking water. How many children are drinking milk?

Let children work independently on the problem. Have them complete the addition sentence when they solve the problem.

For Exercise 2, ask children to draw a picture that shows a different number pair for 10 and to complete the addition sentence to match it.

 Have volunteers explain their drawings and addition sentences to the class.

④ SUMMARIZE MATHEMATICAL PRACTICES

Essential Question

How can you model and write addition sentences for number pairs for sums of 10?

I can use some cubes in one color and then add cubes that are a different color until I have 10. Then I can fill in the numbers I used to write the addition sentence.

Differentiated Instruction — INDEPENDENT ACTIVITIES

Grab-and-Go!

Differentiated Centers Kit

Activities
Together Again!

Children complete the blue Activity Card 18 by modeling addition with two groups of shapes and writing the corresponding addition sentence.

Literature
Flowers for Flossie

 Children read the book and count and add flowers of different colors.

Games
Spin to Add

 Children use connecting cubes to model addition problems.

Digital Path

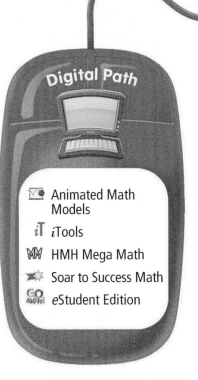

- 📺 Animated Math Models
- iT *iTools*
- ꟽ HMH Mega Math
- ⭐ Soar to Success Math
- 🔵 *eStudent Edition*

Lesson 5.12   216

Summative Assessment

Use the **Chapter Review/Test** to assess children's progress in Chapter 5.

You may wish to review with children the essential question for the chapter.

Chapter Essential Question

How can you show addition?

Ask the following questions to focus children's thinking:

- **How can using objects or pictures help you show addition?**

- **How can you use numbers and symbols to show addition?**

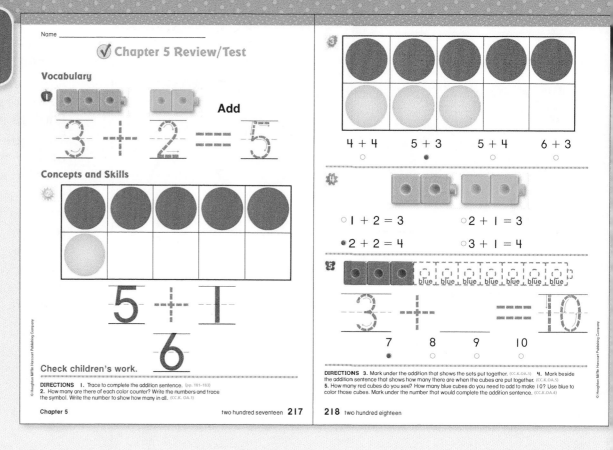

Data-Driven Decision Making

Based on the results of the Chapter Review/Test use the following resources to review skills.

Item	Lesson	*CCSS	Common Error	Intervene With	Soar to Success Math
1	5.4	CC.K.OA.5	May add incorrectly	R—5.4; **TE** —p. 181B	10.03
2	5.2	CC.K.OA.1	May write a sum for one of the addends	R—5.2; **TE**—p. 173B	
3	5.2	CC.K.OA.1	May mark the wrong expression	R—5.2; **TE**—p. 173B	
4	5.4	CC.K.OA.5	May have trouble matching an addition sentence to a set	R—5.4; **TE**—p. 181B	10.03
5	5.5	CC.K.OA.4	May add incorrectly	R—5.5; **TE**—p. 185B	
6	5.6	CC.K.OA.5	May have difficulty understanding a missing addend	R—5.6; **TE**—p. 189B	10.04
7	5.7	CC.K.OA.2	May put the sum as the missing addend	R—5.7; **TE**—p. 193B	10.09
8	5.10	CC.K.OA.3	May have trouble matching an addition sentence to a set	R—5.10; **TE**—p. 205B	10.09

*CCSS—Common Core State Standard   **Key: R**—Reteach Book; **TE**—RtI Activities

Name _____

6

$1 + \underline{} = 3$

1	2	3	4
○	●	○	○

7

$\underline{} + 5 = 8$

1	2	3	4
○	○	●	○

8

● $8 = 2 + 6$	○ $8 = 3 + 5$
○ $8 = 4 + 4$	○ $8 = 5 + 3$

DIRECTIONS 6. Tell an addition word problem about the sets. How many are being added to the set? Mark under the number that would complete the addition sentence. (CC.K.OA.5) 7. Tell an addition word problem about the sets. How many are in the set to start with? Mark under the number that would complete the addition sentence. (CC.K.OA.2) 8. Mark beside the addition sentence that shows the number pair for the cube train. (CC.K.OA.3)

© Houghton Mifflin Harcourt Publishing Company

Chapter 5   two hundred nineteen **219**

Performance Task

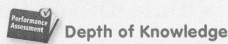

$3 + 2 = 5$

$4 = \underline{} + \underline{}$

$4 = \underline{} + \underline{}$

Check children's work.

DIRECTIONS These tasks will assess the child's understanding of addition. (CC.K.OA.1, CC.K.OA.2, CC.K.OA.3, CC.K.OA.4, CC.K.OA.5)

© Houghton Mifflin Harcourt Publishing Company

220 two hundred twenty

Performance Task

Objective Assess the understanding of addition.

Materials connecting cubes

Listen and Do

Show children Problem 1.

- **Tell an addition word problem about the blimps.**
- **Circle the set you start with. How many are being added to the set? How many are there now?**
- **Write and trace the numbers to complete the addition sentence.**

Draw children's attention to the problem below the line. Give each child eight connecting cubes, four each of two colors.

- **Place two colors of cubes on the cube train to show pairs of numbers that make 4.**
- **Complete the addition sentence to show a number pair for 4. Then show another pair for 4.**
- **Color the cube train to match your second addition sentence.**

Use performance indicators, scoring rubric, and DOK level to evaluate conceptual understanding.

Depth of Knowledge

Performance Task	DOK Level
	2

Performance Assessment

Chapters 1–8

See *Assessment Guide* for Performance Tasks to be completed at the end of each critical area.

Performance Indicators

A child with a Level 2 paper:

____ matches the addition sentence to the objects.

____ completes the addition sentence.

____ completes the addition sentence.

Performance Task Scoring Rubric

2	**Generally accurate, complete, and clear:** All of the parts of the task are successfully completed. There is evidence of clear understanding of the key concepts and procedures. Child's work shows that all answers are correct or reasonable.
1	**Partially accurate:** Some of the tasks are successfully completed; other parts are attempted and their intent addressed, but they are not completed.
0	**Not accurate, complete, and clear:** No part of the task is completed with any success. There is little, if any, evidence that the child understands key concepts and procedures.

 Performance Task may be used for portfolios.

Chapter 5
Test

Summative Assessment

Use the **Chapter Test** to assess children's progress in Chapter 5.

Chapter tests are provided in multiple-choice and mixed-response format in the *Assessment Guide*.

GO Online Chapter 5 Test is available online.

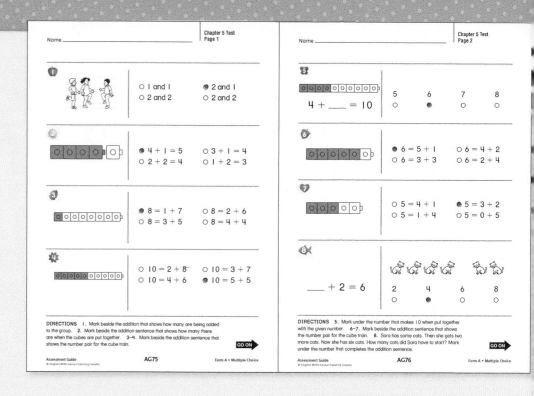

Data-Driven Decision Making ▲RtI

Item	Lesson	*CCSS	Common Error	Intervene With	Soar to Success Math
1	5.1	CC.K.OA.1	May not be able to relate addition expressions to models of sums to 5	R—5.1; TE—p. 169B	
2, 11	5.4	CC.K.OA.5	May not understand how an addition sentence relates to a model	R—5.4; TE—p. 181B	10.03
3	5.10	CC.K.OA.3	May not recognize number pairs that have the sum of 8	R—5.10; TE—p. 205B	10.09
4	5.12	CC.K.OA.3	May not recognize number pairs that have the sum of 10	R—5.12; TE—p. 213B	10.09

*CCSS—Common Core State Standard   **Key: R**—Reteach Book; **TE**—RtI Activities

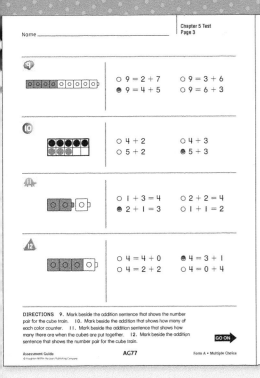

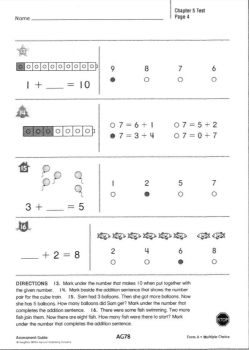

Portfolio Suggestions The portfolio represents the growth, talents, achievements, and reflections of the mathematics learner. Children might spend a short time selecting work samples for their portfolios and completing A Guide to My Math Portfolio from the *Assessment Guide*.

You may want to have children respond to the following questions:

- **How do you think you did on this test?**
- **What would you like to learn more about?**

For information about how to organize, share, and evaluate portfolios, see the *Assessment Guide*.

✓ Data-Driven Decision Making ▲ RtI

Item	Lesson	*CCSS	Common Error	Intervene With	Soar to Success Math
5, 13	5.5	CC.K.OA.4	May not recognize numbers that make a 10	R—5.5; **TE**—p. 185B	
6, 14	5.9	CC.K.OA.3	May not recognize number pairs that have a sum 6 or 7	R—5.9; **TE**—p. 201B	10.09
7, 12	5.8	CC.K.OA.3	May not recognize number pairs that have a sum of 3, 4, or 5	R—5.8; **TE**—p. 197B	10.09
8, 16	5.7	CC.K.OA.2	May have difficulty completing an addition sentence to 10 for a word problem	R—5.7; **TE**—p. 193B	10.09
9	5.11	CC.K.OA.3	May not recognize number pairs that have a sum of 9	R—5.11; **TE**—p. 209B	10.09
10	5.2	CC.K.OA.1	May not be able to relate addition expressions to models of sums from 6 to 10	R—5.2; **TE**—p. 173B	
15	5.6	CC.K.OA.5	May have difficulty completing an addition sentence to 5 for a word problem	R—5.6; **TE**—p. 189B	10.04

*CCSS—Common Core State Standard   **Key: R**—Reteach Book; **TE**—RtI Activities